Mental Disease among Jews

in New York State

BENJAMIN MALZBERG, Ph.D.
Research Foundation for Mental Hygiene, Inc.
and New York State Department of Mental Hygiene

19  60

Intercontinental Medical Book Corporation
New York

Library of Congress Card Catalog No. 60-11073

Intercontinental Medical Book Corporation
381 Park Avenue South, New York 16, N. Y.

Printed and bound in the United States of America

Contents

Preface

THE regulations of the New York State Department of Mental Hygiene require that the State hospitals for mental disease and the licensed private hospitals in New York State all submit statistical reports to the Department, which include data for patients admitted to and under treatment in these hospitals. Since 1912, these data have furnished the basis for a long series of investigations into statistical aspects of mental disease. In 1956, the National Institute of Mental Health, of the National Institutes of Health, United States Public Health Service, made it possible to consider these subjects in a more comprehensive and systematic manner, by providing a research grant to support an inquiry into the distribution of mental disease in New York State. A major part of the investigation is concerned with the relative frequency of mental disease among the larger ethnic aggregates of population in the State. Among these is the Jewish population, which probably constitutes the largest such group in the world today. Nowhere else, not even in Israel, is there available for the study of mental disease among Jews, a body of data equal to that for New York State. For the purposes of this study, I have utilized data for first admissions to all hospitals for mental disease in New York State during fiscal years 1939-1941, inclusive. I am grateful to the New York State Department of Mental Hygiene for permission to use these data, and to the National Institute of Mental Health for the grant which made the study possible.

BENJAMIN MALZBERG, PH.D.

PART I

General Introduction

IN a heterogeneous population such as that of New York State, the incidence of mental disease varies significantly among the larger aggregates. One of the largest of these is the Jewish. Whether they constitute a biological (ethnic) unity is a matter of dispute. It is certain, however, that because so large a proportion derive from eastern Europe, notably Russia and Poland, where, because of historical factors, Jews formed a close-knit, practically endogamous group, they present less variation with respect to physical and mental characteristics than some other populations. Hence, it is a matter of importance, in connection with the study of mental diseases to see how the incidence of such diseases varies among Jews, and what differences, if any, exist between Jews and non-Jews.

Undoubtedly, there has been an assumption in the greater part of the literature that the incidence of mental disease among Jews is above the average. Various explanations have been offered for this higher incidence, such as the history of persecution, ghetto life, occupational restrictions, etc. Even where these have been modified, Jews are still said to have a high rate of mental disease. These are all hypothetical matters, and it is preferable to attempt to arrive at a better evaluation of the facts.

Most of the statistics of mental disease among Jews have had little validity until recently. They were usually based upon admissions to a single hospital, without reference to the population from which these admissions were derived. Usually, they took no cognizance of the age structures, or degrees of urbanization. Consequently, no sound conclusions could be drawn from such data.

The only practical approach to this problem is to study the statistics of first (new) admissions to hospitals for mental disease in a definite area, in which both first admissions and the parent populations can be determined. In this respect, New York State is unique, for not only does New York have a large Jewish population, but the statistics of hospital admissions are complete and uniform over many years.

Several limited attempts were made to utilize these data, by reference to first admissions to some of the State mental hospitals in New York City.[1] The first effort to use complete data was for 1919-1921.[2] During that period, the average annual rates of first admissions to all civil State hospitals were

44.7 per 100,000 Jews, and 69.2 per 100,000 non-Jews. A much better comparison was made for 1925, when the data were limited to New York City. In that year, there were 731 Jewish first admissions from New York City to all hospitals for mental disease in New York State, including committed cases to the licensed (private) hospitals, and a total of 3523 non-Jews. The corresponding rates of first admissions were 40.0 for Jews and 78.4 for non-Jews.[3] As the base populations for Jews were undoubtedly underestimated, it followed that the Jewish rate was overestimated, and that for non-Jews underestimated.

Similar comparisons were made for Massachusetts and Illinois, based upon first admissions to State hospitals during 1926-1928, inclusive.[4] The average annual rates per 100,000 population in Massachusetts were 31.2 and 73.6 for Jews and non-Jews, respectively. In Illinois the corresponding rates were 29.6 and 64.2, respectively.

Prior to 1941, the statistics of first admissions to the licensed hospitals in New York State included only committed cases. Hence, statistical analyses for earlier years had to be limited to data from the State hospitals. However, this introduced a serious deficiency in measuring the incidence of mental disease, since first admissions to licensed hospitals are primarily on a voluntary basis, and represent 70 per cent of all admissions to such hospitals. Furthermore, the omission of such statistics is of greater significance for Jews, since a larger proportion of Jewish than of non-Jewish first admissions are to the licensed hospitals. Complete reporting began in 1941, and satisfactory adjustments were made for the two previous years.

The significance of complete reporting is seen from the fact that of 6987 Jewish first admissions during 1939-1941, 24 per cent were to private hospitals, compared with only 13.2 per cent of the 35,576 non-Jewish white first admissions during the same period. If the statistics are limited to the civil State hospitals, Jewish first admissions constituted 14.8 per cent of the total white first admissions. When the licensed hospitals were included, the corresponding percentage rose to 19.6.

It is clear, therefore, that the relative number of first admissions is influenced by the inclusion of admissions to licensed mental hospitals. It will be shown that the relative distribution of types of mental disorders is also influenced thereby, since the licensed hospitals exercise selection with respect to the admission of some categories of mental disease.

The present analysis of the statistical distribution of mental diseases among Jews is based upon first admissions to all mental hospitals in New York State during three fiscal years, 1939-1941, inclusive. There were 6987 such admissions, of which 5263, or 75 per cent, were to the civil State hospitals, 50, or 0.7 per cent, to the 2 hospitals for criminal insane, and 1674, or 24.0 per cent, to the licensed hospitals. There were 35,576 non-Jewish white first admissions, of which, 30,405, or 85.4 per cent, were to the civil State hospitals, 458, or 1.3 per cent, to the hospitals for criminal insane, and 4713, or 13.2 per cent, to the licensed hospitals.

TABLE 1—Jewish and non-Jewish white first admissions to all hospitals for mental disease in New York State, 1939-1941, classified according to type of hospital and nativity.

	Jews		Non-Jews		Native Jews		Native non-Jews		Foreign-born Jews		Foreign-born non-Jews	
	No.	Per cent	No.	Per cent	No.	Per cent	No.	Per cent	No.	Per cent	No.	Per cent
Civil State hospitals	5263	75.3	30405	85.4	2240	71.5	20201	82.8	3023	78.4	10204	91.3
Hospitals for criminal insane	50	0.7	458	1.3	30	1.0	355	1.4	20	0.5	103	0.9
Licensed hospitals	1674	24.0	4713	13.2	861	27.5	3843	15.8	813	21.1	870	7.8
Total	6987	100.0	35576	100.0	3131	100.0	24399	100.0	3856	100.0	11177	100.0

TABLE 2—White first admissions to all hospitals for mental disease in New York State, 1939-1941, classified according to mental disorder.

Mental disorders	Jews					Non-Jews				
	Males	Females	Total No.	Total Per cent	Average annual rate per 100,000	Males	Females	Total No.	Total Per cent	Average annual rate per 100,000
General paresis	146	51	197	2.8	3.0	1553	490	2043	5.7	6.4
With other syphilis, etc.	26	8	34	0.5	0.5	247	90	337	1.0	1.1
With epidemic encephalitis	27	11	38	0.5	0.6	74	50	124	0.3	0.4
With other infectious disease	10	13	23	0.3	0.3	50	74	124	0.4	0.4
Alcoholic	38	4	42	0.6	0.6	2214	431	2645	7.4	8.3
Due to drugs, etc.	6	9	15	0.2	0.2	71	67	138	0.4	0.4
Traumatic	18	7	25	0.4	0.4	254	46	300	0.8	0.9
With cerebral arteriosclerosis	512	622	1134	16.2	17.1	3694	2901	6595	18.5	20.6
With other disturbances of circulation	17	28	45	0.7	0.7	120	148	268	0.8	0.8
With convulsive disorders	42	30	72	1.0	1.1	314	232	546	1.5	1.7
Senile	174	356	530	7.6	8.0	1702	2317	4019	11.3	12.6
Involutional	158	463	621	8.9	9.4	710	1576	2286	6.4	7.1
Due to other metabolic, etc.	20	15	35	0.5	0.5	50	113	163	0.4	0.5
Due to new growth	14	32	46	0.7	0.7	73	39	112	0.3	0.3
With organic changes, etc.	36	29	65	0.9	1.0	130	105	235	0.7	0.7
Manic-depressive	238	616	854	12.2	12.9	850	1681	2531	7.1	7.9
Dementia praecox	1012	1140	2152	30.8	32.5	4114	3847	7961	22.4	24.9
Paranoia & paranoid conditions	32	33	65	0.9	1.0	152	198	350	1.0	1.1
With psychopathic personality	75	39	114	1.6	1.7	493	182	675	1.9	2.1
With mental deficiency	80	87	167	2.4	2.5	412	365	777	2.2	2.4
Psychoneuroses	250	300	550	7.9	8.3	757	991	1748	4.9	5.5
Undiagnosed	23	22	45	0.6	0.7	142	120	262	0.7	0.8
Without psychosis	59	20	79	1.1	1.2	803	336	1139	3.2	3.5
Primary behavior disorders	30	9	39	0.6	0.6	133	65	198	0.6	0.6
Total	3043	3944	6987	100.0	105.6	19112	16464	35576	100.0	111.1

Table 2 shows the classification of the first admissions with respect to types of mental disorders. Of the total Jews, 2152, or 30.8 per cent, were diagnosed as dementia praecox. Other groups were as follows: Psychoses with cerebral arteriosclerosis, 1134, or 16.2 per cent; manic-depressive psychoses, 854, or 12.2 per cent; involutional psychoses, 621, or 8.9 per cent; senile psychoses, 530, or 7.6 per cent; psychoneuroses, 550, or 7.9 per cent.

Dementia praecox was also the leading category among non-Jewish white first admissions, representing 22.4 per cent of the total of 35,576 such first admissions. Psychoses with cerebral arteriosclerosis followed with 6595 cases, or 18.5 per cent of the total. Other large groups were as follows: senile psychoses, 4019, or 11.3 per cent; alcoholic psychoses, 2645, or 7.4 per cent; manic-depressive psychoses, 2531, or 7.1 per cent; involutional psychoses, 2286, or 6.4 per cent; general paresis, 2043, or 5.7 per cent.

We may combine the mental disorders into those of organic origin, and those termed functional. Among the former, we may include general paresis, alcoholic psychoses, senile psychoses, and psychoses with cerebral arteriosclerosis. This group included 27.2 per cent of the total Jewish first admissions, and 42.9 per cent of the non-Jewish first admissions. The functional group includes involutional psychoses, manic-depressive psychoses, dementia praecox, and psychoneuroses. This group included 59.8 per cent of the Jewish first admissions, but only 40.8 per cent of the non-Jewish first admissions.

Obviously, there is a fundamental difference between Jews and non-Jews in the distribution of the mental disorders, the former tending towards the functional disorders, the latter toward psychoses of organic origin.

The distribution of the types is influenced by the nativity of the first admissions. Thus, dementia praecox included 46.4 per cent of the native Jewish first admissions, but only 18.1 per cent of the foreign-born. On the other hand, senile psychoses and psychoses with cerebral arteriosclerosis included 12.4 and 26.8 per cent, respectively, of the foreign Jewish first admissions, but only 1.6 and 3.2 per cent of native Jews. Similar differences, though of lesser degree, occurred among the non-Jews. Obviously, these are related to differences in age distribution of natives and foreign-born.

The influence of age may be seen further in the fact that only 7.5 per cent of native Jewish first admissions were included in diagnoses of organic origin, whereas 76.4 per cent were in the 4 functional categories. Among foreign-born Jews, the corresponding percentages were 43.2 and 46.3, respectively. Differences of a similar character occurred among non-Jews.

We have been discussing the proportionate distribution of mental disease, but this is not the equivalent of rates of first admissions. From the fact that dementia praecox constitutes a higher percentage of all first admissions among Jews than among non-Jews, it cannot be concluded that Jews have a higher rate of dementia praecox. Nor can it be said that Jews have a lower rate of first admissions with alcoholic psychoses, because the percentage with such psychoses is lower. Percentages and rates have often been confused. The true rate is obtained, not from the proportional distribution of such psychoses, but from the ratio of first admissions to the population from whom they were derived; in other words, the number of first admissions per 100,000 corresponding general population.

It is necessary, therefore, in addition to statistics of first admissions, to have a measure of the general population. There is no official (governmental) census of the population according to ethnic groups (other than by color) in the United States. One must, therefore, estimate the Jewish population, and this has been attempted through varying procedures.

TABLE 3—Native Jewish and non-Jewish white first admissions to all hospitals for mental disease in New York State, 1939-1941, classified according to mental disorders.

Mental disorders	Number						Per cent					
	Jews			Non-Jews			Jews			Non-Jews		
	Males	Females	Total	Males	Females	Total	Males	Females	Total	Males	Females	Total
General paresis	55	15	70	883	370	1253	3.6	0.9	2.2	6.9	3.2	5.1
With other syphilis, etc.	12	3	15	140	65	205	0.8	0.2	0.5	1.1	0.6	0.8
With epidemic encephalitis	15	7	22	61	43	104	1.0	0.4	0.7	0.4	0.4	0.4
With other infectious diseases	2	4	6	32	62	94	0.1	0.2	0.2	0.2	0.5	0.4
Alcoholic	15	—	15	1522	269	1791	1.0	—	0.5	11.8	2.3	7.3
Due to drugs, etc.	6	3	9	56	56	112	0.4	0.2	0.3	0.4	0.4	0.4
Traumatic	3	1	4	153	31	184	0.2	0.1	0.1	1.2	0.3	0.8
With cerebral arteriosclerosis	50	51	101	2003	1757	3760	3.3	3.1	3.2	15.5	15.3	15.4
With other disturbances of circulation	2	7	9	80	102	182	0.1	0.4	0.3	0.6	0.9	0.7
With convulsive disorders	24	14	38	244	200	444	1.6	0.9	1.2	1.9	1.7	1.8
Senile	18	31	49	933	1326	2259	1.2	1.9	1.6	7.2	11.5	9.3
Involutional	30	94	124	444	935	1379	2.0	5.8	4.0	3.4	8.1	5.7
Due to other metabolic, etc.	8	4	12	33	83	116	0.5	0.2	0.4	0.3	0.7	0.5
Due to new growth	6	2	8	46	26	72	0.4	0.1	0.3	0.4	0.2	0.3
With organic changes, etc.	15	14	29	92	87	179	1.0	0.9	0.9	0.7	0.8	0.7
Manic-depressive	138	357	495	652	1308	1960	9.2	22.0	15.8	5.1	11.4	8.0
Dementia praecox	745	708	1453	3117	2907	6024	49.4	43.6	46.4	24.2	25.3	24.7
Paranoia & paranoid conditions	10	13	23	85	142	227	0.7	0.8	0.7	0.7	1.2	0.9
With psychopathic personality	56	28	84	412	155	567	3.7	1.7	2.7	3.2	1.3	2.3
With mental deficiency	62	61	123	354	318	672	4.1	3.8	3.9	2.7	2.8	2.8
Psychoneuroses	153	166	319	599	818	1417	10.1	10.2	10.2	4.6	7.1	5.8
Undiagnosed	17	14	31	113	101	214	1.1	0.9	1.0	0.9	0.9	0.9
Without psychosis	37	16	53	709	290	999	2.4	1.0	1.7	5.5	2.5	4.1
Primary behavior disorders	30	9	39	127	58	185	2.0	0.6	1.2	1.0	0.5	0.8
Total	1509	1622	3131	12890	11509	24399	100.0	100.0	100.0	100.0	100.0	100.0

TABLE 4—Foreign-born Jewish and non-Jewish white first admissions to all hospitals for mental disease in New York State, 1939-1941, classified according to mental disorders.

Mental disorders	Number						Per cent					
	Jews			Non-Jews			Jews			Non-Jews		
	Males	Fe-males	Total	Males	Fe-males	Total	Males	Fe-males	Total	Males	Fe-males	Total
General paresis	91	36	127	670	120	790	5.9	1.6	3.3	10.8	2.4	7.1
With other syphilis, etc.	14	5	19	107	25	132	0.9	0.2	0.5	1.7	0.5	1.1
With epidemic encephalitis	12	4	16	13	7	20	0.8	0.2	0.4	0.2	0.1	0.2
With other infectious diseases	8	9	17	18	12	30	0.5	0.4	0.4	0.3	0.2	0.3
Alcoholic	23	4	27	692	162	854	1.5	0.2	0.7	11.1	3.3	7.6
Due to drugs, etc.	—	6	6	15	11	26	—	0.3	0.2	0.2	0.2	0.2
Traumatic	15	6	21	101	15	116	1.0	0.3	0.5	1.6	0.3	1.0
With cerebral arteriosclerosis	462	571	1033	1691	1144	2835	30.1	24.6	26.8	27.2	23.1	25.4
With other disturbances of circulation	15	21	36	40	46	86	1.0	0.9	0.9	0.7	0.9	0.8
With convulsive disorders	18	16	34	70	32	102	1.2	0.7	0.9	1.1	0.7	0.9
Senile	156	325	481	769	991	1760	10.2	14.0	12.4	12.4	20.0	15.7
Involutional	128	369	497	266	641	907	8.3	15.9	12.9	4.3	12.9	8.1
Due to other metabolic, etc.	12	11	23	17	30	47	0.8	0.4	0.6	0.3	0.6	0.4
Due to new growth	8	30	38	27	13	40	0.5	1.3	1.0	0.4	0.3	0.4
With organic changes, etc.	21	15	36	38	18	56	1.4	0.6	0.9	0.6	0.4	0.5
Manic-depressive	100	259	359	198	373	571	6.5	11.2	9.3	3.2	7.5	5.1
Dementia praecox	267	432	699	997	940	1937	17.4	18.6	18.1	16.0	19.0	17.3
Paranoia & paranoid conditions	22	20	42	67	56	123	1.4	0.9	1.1	1.1	1.1	1.1
With psychopathic personality	19	11	30	81	27	108	1.2	0.4	0.8	1.3	0.5	1.0
With mental deficiency	18	26	44	58	47	105	1.2	1.1	1.1	0.9	1.0	0.9
Psychoneuroses	97	134	231	158	173	331	6.3	5.8	6.0	2.5	3.5	3.0
Undiagnosed	6	8	14	29	19	48	0.4	0.3	0.4	0.4	0.4	0.4
Without psychosis	22	4	26	94	46	140	1.4	0.2	0.7	1.5	0.9	1.3
Primary behavior disorders	—	—	—	6	7	13	—	—	—	0.1	0.1	0.1
Total	1534	2322	3856	6222	4955	11177	100.0	100.0	100.0	100.0	100.0	100.0

The earliest estimates were based upon the decennial census of church affiliations. Statistics of membership in synagogues and temples were compiled and these were equated to the Jewish population. Obviously, even if such lists were reported accurately they nevertheless furnished no basis for estimating the Jews who were not so affiliated.

In large centers of population, such as cities, the Jewish population has been estimated by establishing a ratio between the number of Jewish children in school and the total Jewish population. The number of Jewish children was estimated by counting the absences from school on the Day of Atonement (Yom Kippur). It was assumed that practically all Jewish children are absent on that day. By comparing with the average number of daily absences, the total was then adjusted so as to exclude the presumably non-Jewish element. The ratio of Jewish school children to the (unknown) total Jewish population was assumed to equal the ratio of all children of school age in the given community to the total population as usually given by the federal census of population. It has been shown, however, that this method results in an underestimation of the Jewish population by almost 20 per cent, as Jewish children form a smaller proportion of the total Jewish population than is true of the total population.[5]

A method similar in principal is that of estimating the Jewish population through a consideration of the number of Jewish deaths. The ratio of deaths to the unknown population of similar age is assumed to be the same as the corresponding death rate for the general population. Jewish deaths are identified from death records by picking out so-called Jewish names, by counting burials in cemeteries where only Jews are interred, and by checking the records of undertakers who are known to officiate at almost all Jewish funerals. Assuming the essential accuracy of such an enumeration of deaths, it still results in underestimating the Jewish population through the assumption that Jews have the same age specific death rates as the general population. This error was overcome in large part in the study of New York City in 1927[6] by finding death rates in certain areas of the city which were known to be predominantly Jewish. These death rates were then applied to the total Jewish deaths, as determined from official records. The determination of Jews was mostly by name.

In smaller places, when it is feasible, counts of Jewish populations are made by enquiries of key individuals in the community. In larger areas, however, enumerations begin by reference to master lists of Jewish names. These lists include the names of members of Jewish organizations, such as synagogues, temples, welfare and fraternal organizations, etc. When a census of the Jewish population of a city is undertaken, it usually begins with a study of the lists, from which duplicates are removed. To these lists are added new names, obtained through systematic enquiries in all sections of the city. Finally, in some cities, such as Buffalo in 1938, an actual house by house enquiry is made in selected areas of the city. From all such sources, a final estimate is arrived at. In the nature of the case, the estimate must fall short of the true total, though the degree of incompleteness is not known. In those cities where actual counts have been made, it is not likely that the error is greater than 10 per cent, but the error is always an underestimate.

There was no estimate of the number of Jews in New York State in 1940. The closest approximation was for 1937. In that year, the Jewish population was estimated at 2,206,328.[7] This was obtained by combining estimates for New York City with those for the remainder of the State. The former was obtained through use of the Yom Kippur method with an adjustment based upon statistics of the foreign-born according to mother-tongue. Estimates for the remainder of the state were obtained from key individuals in small communities and by approximations in larger places by methods outlined above. In the nature of the case, it is certain that totals for both State and City are too low. By using as base the estimated Jewish population for 1937, we are, furthermore excluding the increase that must have occurred between 1937 and 1940. Therefore, all rates obtained by use of the estimate for 1937 are too high. Since the total non-Jewish white population was obtained by subtracting the estimated Jewish population from the total white population in 1940 as given by the federal census, corresponding rates of first admissions for non-Jews must be too low. If, therefore, it is shown, on the basis of an underestimated general Jewish population that rates of first admissions are lower for Jews than for non-Jews, it must follow that the correct differences in 1940 are still greater.

We have no data giving the distribution of Jews in New York State in 1937 according to age and sex. No attempts have been made to estimate the sex proportions. The age distribution, however, does exercise a significant influence upon rates of first admissions. An approximation was therefore necessary. This was derived from the age distributions of Jews in 10 cities of varying size in the United States, as shown in a volume entitled "Jewish Population Studies", edited by Sophia M. Robison.[8] These 10 cities had an estimated total of 506,700 Jews. The average age distribution of this total is shown, in per cent, in Table 5.

TABLE 5—Age distribution of a sample of urban Jewish populations in 10 cities in the United States, and in Montreal and Toronto, in per cent.

Age (years)	United States*	Montreal (1941)	Tooronto (1941)
Under 5	6.1	6.9	6.2
5–9	6.6	6.6	6.9
10–14	7.2	7.5	7.7
15–19	7.8	8.7	9.1
20–24	9.1	9.1	9.8
25–34	18.7	21.6	21.2
35–44	17.2	15.3	14.9
45–54	14.0	11.7	11.8
55–64	8.3	7.7	7.6
65 and over	5.0	4.9	4.8
Total	100.0	100.0	100.0

* 10 cities, not including New York City, circa 1937

It was assumed that the age distribution of Jews in New York State was not essentially different from that shown for Jews throughout the United States, in Table 5. This is a reasonable assumption, as the individual cities did not vary radically in their age distributions. Furthermore, it is possible to compare this age distribution with similar distributions for Canada, where the population is not estimated, but is actually enumerated with respect to religion, and ethnic origin, in connection with the census of population. Montreal had a Jewish population of 51,132 in 1941.[9] The Jewish population of Toronto totaled 48,744.[10] It may be observed in Table 5 that there is no essential difference in the age distribution of Jews in Montreal and Toronto, and both are reasonably close to the distribution of Jewish population of the United States. If the populations are grouped into age classes of importance with respect to the relative distribution of mental disease, we find a very close similarity, as follows:

TABLE 6—Age distribution of urban Jewish populations, in per cent.

Age (years)	United States	Montreal	Toronto
Under 15	19.9	21.0	20.8
15–44	52.8	54.7	55.0
45–64	22.3	19.4	19.4
65 and over	5.0	4.9	4.8
Total	100.0	100.0	100.0

We are therefore assuming the essential validity of the age distribution for Jews, as shown in Table 5. Applying this to the estimated total Jewish population of New York State, we obtain the numerical distribution of Jews, by age. Subtracting this from the corresponding white population of New York State, as given in the census of 1940, we obtained the estimated non-Jewish white population, by age. These are shown in Table 7.

TABLE 7—Estimated Jewish and non-Jewish white population of New York State, 1940.

Age (years)	Total white	Jews	Non-Jews
Under 5	796,654	134,586	662,068
5–9	851,692	145,618	706,074
10–14	999,353	158,856	840,497
15–19	1,078,225	172,094	906,131
20–24	1,093,638	200,776	892,862
25–34	2,197,086	412,583	1,784,503
35–44	2,060,037	379,488	1,680,549
45–54	1,753,343	308,886	1,444,457
55–64	1,144,646	183,125	961,521
65 and over	904,872	110,316	794,556
Total	12,879,546	2,206,328	10,673,218

On the basis of the estimated population, the average annual rate of first admissions was 105.6 per 100,000 Jews. Among the leading categories, the average annual rates were as follows: dementia praecox, 32.5; psychoses with cerebral arteriosclerosis, 17.1; manic-depressive psychoses, 12.9; involutional psychoses, 9.4; psychoneuroses, 8.3. The rate for alcoholic psychoses was only 0.6. General paresis was also low, with a rate of 3.0.

The non-Jewish white population had an average annual rate of 111.1. The rates occurred in the following order: dementia praecox, 24.9; psychoses with cerebral arteriosclerosis, 20.6; senile psychoses, 12.6; alcoholic psychoses, 8.3; manic-depressive psychoses, 7.9; involutional psychoses, 7.1; general paresis, 6.4.

Jews had higher rates with respect to the functional disorders and lower rates for those of organic origin. For the latter (general paresis, alcoholic, psychoses with cerebral arteriosclerosis, and senile psychoses), the average annual rates were 28.8 and 47.8 per 100,000 Jews and non-Jews, respectively. For the functional group (involutional, manic-depressive, dementia praecox, psychoneuroses), the average annual rates per 100,000 were 63.1 and 45.4, respectively.

In general, it is indicated that the total rate of first admissions is lower for Jews. The rates vary, however, with respect to diagnosis.

Rates of first admissions are influenced by the age composition of the general population. Young populations, other things equal, have a low rate of first admissions; older populations have higher rates. It is necessary, therefore, to consider age specific rates. Such rates are shown in Table 8.

TABLE 8—Jewish and non-Jewish white first admissions to all hospitals for mental diseased in New York State, 1939-1941, classified according to age and rate per 100,000 population.

Age (years)	Jews					Non-Jews				
	Males	Females	Total		Average annual rate per 100,000	Males	Females	Total		Average annual rate per 100,000
			No.	Per cent				No.	Per cent	
Under 10	31	8	39	0.6	4.6	68	26	94	0.3	2.3
10–14	40	18	58	0.8	12.2	109	69	178	0.5	7.1
15–19	269	203	472	6.8	91.4	636	543	1179	3.3	43.4
20–24	336	324	660	9.4	109.6	1202	965	2167	6.1	80.9
25–34	581	747	1328	19.0	107.3	2858	2691	5549	15.6	103.7
35–44	478	714	1192	17.1	104.7	3471	2790	6261	17.6	124.2
45–54	421	687	1108	15.9	119.6	3476	2733	6209	17.4	143.3
55–64	359	506	865	12.4	157.4	2779	2156	4935	13.9	171.1
65 and over	528	737	1265	18.1	382.2	4513	4491	9004	25.3	377.7
Total	3043	3944	6987	100.0	105.6	19112	16464	35576	100.0	111.1

Among Jews, they rose, with minor fluctuations, from 4.6 per 100,000 at ages under 10 to 382.2 at 65 and over. Among non-Jews, they rose similarly with age to a maximum of 377.7 at 65 and over. Below age 35, Jews had higher rates of first admissions. Beyond age 35, rates were generally higher for non-Jews. This difference is related to the relative distribution of types of mental disorders. The functional psychoses which are relatively more frequent among Jewish first admissions, occur in early life, whereas those of organic origin occur primarily at older ages.

The average annual rate was 105.6 per 100,000 Jews, compared to 111.1 for non-Jews. However, we must consider the effect of the age distributions. This may be done by standardizing the rates, using as standard the white population of New York State on April 1, 1940, aged 15 and over, in appropriate age intervals. On this basis, the rates became 137.4 for Jews and 137.6 for non-Jews. In addition to age, however, we must consider that Jews are primarily an urban population, of whom 92 per cent were in New York City. Of the non-Jews, only 46 per cent were in New York City. It has been shown repeatedly that rates of first admissions are higher for urban populations in general, and for New York City in particular.[11] The more legitimate comparison, therefore, is between Jews and non-Jews in New York City.

For this purpose we again require the age distributions of the two populations. Jews in New York City were estimated to number 2,035,000 in 1937.[12] Because of their concentration in New York City, it may be assumed that their age distribution is for all practical purposes the same as that for all Jews in New York State. The resulting age distribution is shown in numbers in Table 9. The total white population of New York City was classified by age in the federal census of 1940. The non-Jewish population was therefore obtained by subtracting the Jews from the corresponding age groups for the total white population. The resulting age distribution is shown in Table 9.

TABLE 9—Estimated Jewish and non-Jewish white population, New York City, 1940.

Age (years)	Total white	Jews	Non-Jews
Under 5	403,239	124,135	279,104
5–9	436,484	134,310	302,174
10–14	524,420	146,520	377,900
15–19	571,412	158,730	412,682
20–24	607,184	185,185	421,999
25–34	1,282,277	380,545	901,732
35–44	1,198,337	350,020	848,317
45–54	962,597	284,900	677,697
55–64	590,026	168,905	421,121
65 and over	401,525	101,750	299,775
Total	6,977,501	2,035,000	4,942,501

Average annual rates of first admissions are shown in Table 10. The rates for Jews did not vary greatly from corresponding rates for all Jews of New York State. This was to be expected since both Jewish first admissions and the Jewish population were predominantly from New York City. In the case of the non-Jews, however, the age specific rates were all significantly higher for New York City than for the State as a whole. Consequently, the average rates for the two populations differed significantly. Jews had a rate of 104.9, compared with 132.1 for non-Jews.

TABLE 10—Jewish and non-Jewish white first admissions from New York City to all hospitals for mental disease in New York State, 1939-1941, classified according to age and rate per 100,000 population.

Age (years)	Jews					Non-Jews				
	Males	Females	Total		Average annual rate per 100,000	Males	Females	Total		Average annual rate per 100,000
			No.	Per cent				No.	Per cent	
Under 10	30	7	37	0.6	4.8	49	18	67	0.3	3.8
10–14	38	17	55	0.9	12.5	55	28	83	0.4	7.3
15–19	249	188	437	6.8	91.8	363	285	648	3.3	52.3
20–24	296	291	587	9.2	105.7	668	533	1201	6.1	94.9
25–34	516	691	1207	18.8	105.7	1629	1497	3126	16.0	115.6
35–44	429	677	1106	17.3	105.3	1995	1521	3516	18.0	138.2
45–54	377	622	999	15.6	116.9	1993	1432	3425	17.5	168.4
55–64	336	463	799	12.4	157.7	1627	1167	2794	14.3	221.2
65 and over	485	694	1179	18.4	386.2	2374	2351	4725	24.1	525.4
Total	2756	3650	6406	100.0	104.9	10753	8832	19585	100.0	132.1

As for the State as a whole, we may standardize the rates for New York City, using the same population as previously for the standard. The standardized rates were 136.7 for Jews and 168.4 for non-Jews. Thus, the rate for the non-Jewish white population was in excess by 23 per cent.

It was emphasized previously that the estimate of the Jewish population was necessarily an underestimate. The number of first admissions to mental hospitals was an actual count, however. Thus, it is clear that the rate for Jews must have been overestimated, and therefore the rate for non-Jews was underestimated. The true differences in rates between Jews and non-Jews in New York State must be greater than 23 per cent, and we conclude that Jews have a significantly lower rate of first admissions to hospitals for mental disease than non-Jews.

Age

Jewish first admissions were younger than non-Jews. They had a smaller proportion at the older ages (i.e., 50 years and over). A significantly larger percentage of Jewish first admissions were at younger ages, especially under 20. Associated with such differences are the relative differences in the distribution of the mental disorders; for example, a higher percentage of Jewish first admissions with dementia praecox. The average age of Jewish first admissions was 44.7 years. Females were significantly older than males, the average ages being 46.0 and 43.1 years, respectively.

Non-Jewish first admissions were older than Jews. They had an average age of 49.8 years, compared with 44.7 years for Jews. Males and females had average ages of 49.3 and 50.4 years, respectively, both greater than corresponding ages for Jews.

TABLE 11—Jewish first admissions to all hospitals for mental disease in New York State, 1939-1941, classified according to age.

Age (years)	Number			Per cent		
	Males	Females	Total	Males	Females	Total
Under 10	31	8	39	1.0	0.2	0.6
10–14	40	18	58	1.3	0.5	0.8
15–19	269	203	472	8.8	5.1	6.8
20–24	336	324	660	11.0	8.2	9.4
25–29	295	396	691	9.7	10.0	9.9
30–34	286	351	637	9.4	8.9	9.1
35–39	229	380	609	7.5	9.6	8.7
40–44	249	334	583	8.2	8.5	8.3
45–49	197	362	559	6.4	9.2	8.0
50–54	224	325	549	7.4	8.2	7.9
55–59	197	264	461	6.4	6.7	6.6
60–64	162	242	404	5.3	6.1	5.8
65–69	173	226	399	5.7	5.7	5.7
70–74	151	201	352	5.0	5.1	5.0
75–79	115	161	276	3.8	4.1	4.0
80–84	55	98	153	1.8	2.5	2.2
85–89	26	32	58	0.9	0.8	0.8
90–94	6	16	22	0.2	0.4	0.3
95–99	2	3	5	0.1	0.1	0.1
Total	3043	3944	6987	100.0	100.0	100.0

Nativity

Of the 6987 Jewish first admissions, 3131, or 44.8 per cent, were native, and 3856, or 55.2 per cent, were foreign-born. The corresponding percentages for non-Jews were 68.6 and 31.4, respectively. Foreign-born Jews are estimated to represent 35 per cent of Jews in the United States.[13] Assuming the same proportion for New York State, it appears, therefore, that foreign-born Jews included more than their expected percentage of first admissions, whereas native Jews were below their quota. This is not conclusive since corresponding rates of first admissions cannot be computed in the absence of appropriate age statistics. However, it is known from previous studies that foreign-born whites have a higher rate of first admissions than native whites.[14]

Of the 3856 foreign-born Jewish first admissions, 1817, or 47 per cent, were from Russia. Other nativity groups, all of a lower numerical order, were: Poland, 627; Austria, 564; Germany, 230; Hungary, 196; Roumania, 141. Of the 3131 native Jewish first admissions, 1471, or 47.0 per cent, had parents who were born in Russia. Thus, 3288, or 47.1 per cent of all Jewish first admissions were of Russian Jewish origin. The corresponding percentage for Poland was 13.4. Studies of the general Jewish population show a similarly high proportion of Russian origin, followed by Poland. We cannot compute rates, however, in the absence of necessary basic data for the Jewish population.

TABLE 12—Non-Jewish white first admissions to all hospitals for mental disease in New York State, 1939-1941, classified according to age.

Age (years)	Number			Per cent		
	Males	Females	Total	Males	Females	Total
Under 5	7	5	12	*	*	*
5–9	61	21	82	0.3	0.1	0.2
10–14	109	69	178	0.6	0.4	0.5
15–19	636	543	1179	3.3	3.3	3.3
20–24	1202	965	2167	6.3	5.9	6.1
25–29	1328	1296	2624	7.0	7.9	7.4
30–34	1530	1395	2925	8.0	8.5	8.2
35–39	1716	1438	3154	9.0	8.7	8.9
40–44	1755	1352	3107	9.2	8.2	8.7
45–49	1727	1384	3111	9.0	8.4	8.7
50–54	1749	1349	3098	9.2	8.2	8.7
55–59	1402	1062	2464	7.3	6.5	6.9
60–64	1377	1094	2471	7.2	6.6	7.0
65–69	1318	1170	2488	6.9	7.1	7.0
70–74	1168	1110	2278	6.1	6.7	6.4
75–79	1048	1046	2094	5.5	6.4	5.9
80–84	660	728	1388	3.5	4.4	3.9
85–89	250	343	593	1.3	2.1	1.7
90–94	60	83	143	0.3	0.5	0.4
95–99	7	10	17	*	0.1	*
100–104	2	1	3	*	*	*
Total	19112	16464	35576	100.0	100.0	100.0

*Less than 0.05.

TABLE 13—Foreign-born Jewish first admissions to all hospitals for mental disease in New York State, 1939-1941, classified according to age and nativity.

Age (years)	Russia			Poland			Austria			Germany			Hungary			Roumania		
	M	F	T	M	F	T	M	F	T	M	F	T	M	F	T	M	F	T
15–19	1	3	4	4	3	7	3	1	4	7	1	8	—	2	2	—	—	—
20–24	8	7	15	10	6	16	5	4	9	2	6	8	—	2	2	—	1	1
25–29	17	30	47	28	20	48	5	10	15	6	14	20	3	2	5	3	4	7
30–34	30	48	78	27	25	52	17	19	36	5	7	12	1	9	10	1	—	1
35–39	38	101	139	25	31	56	9	16	25	2	11	13	6	12	18	2	8	10
40–44	67	110	177	24	48	72	8	19	27	9	7	16	2	15	17	2	15	17
45–49	62	114	176	33	40	73	18	54	72	7	11	18	2	20	22	7	10	17
50–54	87	145	232	34	45	79	24	36	60	3	7	10	4	12	16	8	14	22
55–59	88	116	204	18	33	51	24	34	58	6	9	15	13	12	25	6	8	14
60–64	75	109	184	12	28	40	28	52	80	5	5	10	7	6	13	7	6	13
65–69	73	109	182	18	22	40	22	40	62	12	6	18	12	12	24	5	2	7
70–74	74	82	156	20	24	44	23	28	51	6	16	22	8	11	19	4	9	13
75–79	52	72	124	12	17	29	12	18	30	15	15	30	6	8	14	2	4	6
80–84	17	39	56	8	9	17	12	12	24	2	16	18	3	5	8	5	5	10
85 and over	20	23	43	—	3	3	5	6	11	4	8	12	1	—	1	—	3	3
Total	709	1108	1817	273	354	627	215	349	564	91	139	230	68	128	196	52	89	141

TABLE 14—Native Jewish first admissions to all hospitals for mental disease in New York State, 1939–1941, classified according to age and nativity of parents.

Age (years)	Russia			Poland			Austria			Germany			Hungary			Roumania		
	M	F	T	M	F	T	M	F	T	M	F	T	M	F	T	M	F	T
Under 10	3	2	5	5	1	6	1	2	3	2	—	2	—	1	1	—	—	—
10–14	14	10	24	6	3	9	5	1	6	—	—	—	—	—	—	—	—	—
15–19	117	107	224	29	17	46	27	24	51	—	1	1	6	8	14	14	8	22
20–24	165	165	330	29	33	62	37	38	75	1	2	3	6	6	12	12	13	25
25–29	132	149	281	17	37	54	31	47	78	5	13	18	9	17	26	8	19	27
30–34	92	115	207	21	27	48	29	35	64	8	11	19	8	4	12	10	11	21
35–39	56	94	150	12	21	33	30	29	59	9	5	14	6	7	13	6	7	13
40–44	53	51	104	7	9	16	22	20	42	9	10	19	6	7	13	6	5	11
45–49	25	50	75	3	3	6	13	19	32	3	8	11	5	2	7	—	4	4
50–54	22	9	31	7	6	13	7	7	14	9	9	18	2	6	8	—	—	—
55–59	11	6	17	4	1	5	3	14	17	10	7	17	—	1	1	—	1	1
60–64	8	7	15	1	1	2	1	8	9	6	7	13	1	1	2	—	—	—
65–69	—	2	2	1	—	1	5	—	5	7	10	17	—	—	—	—	—	—
70–74	1	2	3	1	3	4	—	1	1	4	5	9	—	—	—	—	—	—
75–79	—	3	3	1	1	2	—	—	—	8	14	22	1	—	1	—	—	—
80–84	—	—	—	—	—	—	—	—	—	5	3	8	—	—	—	—	—	—
85–89	—	—	—	—	—	—	—	—	—	1	2	3	—	—	—	—	—	—
Total	699	772	1471	144	163	307	211	245	456	87	107	194	50	60	110	56	68	124

Environment

The Bureau of the Census defined the urban population in 1940 as that residing in cities and other incorporated places with 2500 inhabitants or more. The remainder of the population was defined as rural. Those living on a farm were classified as rural-farm. All other rural inhabitants were classified as non-farm.

Jews are predominantly an urban population, as indicated previously. This is reflected in the statistics of first admission. Only 40 of the Jewish first admissions, or 0.6 per cent of the total, were from a rural environment. The overwhelming majority were from New York City. Non-Jewish first admissions were also largely urban, but less so than Jews. Furthermore, only 55.1 per cent were from New York City, whereas 35.1 per cent were from the remaining urban areas. Native Jews were relatively more prevalent than foreign Jews in areas outside New York City. This was true to an even larger degree among non-Jews.

TABLE 15—Jewish and non-Jewish white first admissions to all hospitals for mental disease in New York State, 1939-1941, classified according to environment and nativity.

Environment	Jews		Non-Jews		Native Jews		Native non-Jews		Foreign-born Jews		Foreign-born non-Jews	
	No.	Per cent	No.	Per cent	No.	Per cent	No.	Per cent	No.	Per cent	No.	Per cent
Urban	6947	99.4	32085	90.2	3107	99.2	21367	87.6	3840	99.6	10718	95.9
New York City	6406	91.7	19585	55.1	2807	89.7	11515	47.2	3598	93.3	8071	72.2
Other	541	7.7	12500	35.1	300	9.6	9852	40.4	242	6.3	2647	23.7
Rural	40	0.6	3491	9.8	24	0.8	3032	12.4	16	0.4	459	4.1
Farm	6	0.1	981	2.8	3	0.1	864	3.5	3	0.1	117	1.0
Non-farm	34	0.5	2510	7.1	21	0.7	2168	8.9	13	0.3	342	3.1
Total	6987	100.0	35576	100.0	3131	100.0	24399	100.0	3856	100.0	11177	100.0

Use of alcohol

Of the Jewish first admissions, 2.4 per cent were intemperate users of alcohol, compared with 18.8 per cent of non-Jews. If we omit those with alcoholic psychoses, the corresponding percentages for the remaining first admissions were: Jews, 1.9; non-Jews, 12.2. Thus, not only do Jews have a lower rate of alcoholic psychoses than non-Jews (as will be shown subsequently), but in general there is less intemperance among Jews. This verifies once again an oft-noted phenomenon. It would be of importance to compare drinking habits among native Jews with those of foreign-born Jews. There is a general impression that the newer generation of Jews indulges more than the older generation of Jews in the use of alcoholic beverages, but whether to a degree resulting in high rates of intemperance is not well established. More intensive studies on a larger scale are necessary to establish such a trend, if it exists.

TABLE 16—Jewish and non-Jewish white first admissions to all hospitals for mental disease in New York State, 1939-1941, classified according to use of alcohol and nativity.

Use of alcohol	Jews		Non-Jews		Native Jews		Native non-Jews		Foreign-born Jews		Foreign-born non-Jews	
	No.	Per cent	No.	Per cent	No.	Per cent	No.	Per cent	No.	Per cent	No.	Per cent
Abstinent	5199	74.4	16755	47.1	2267	72.4	11973	49.1	2929	76.0	4785	42.8
Moderate	1278	18.3	10570	29.7	621	19.8	6814	27.9	643	16.7	3770	33.7
Intemperate	173	2.4	6679	18.8	76	2.4	4525	18.5	99	2.6	2152	19.3
Unascertained	337	4.8	1572	4.4	167	5.3	1087	4.5	185	4.8	470	4.2
Total	6987	100.0	35576	100.0	3131	100.0	24399	100.0	3856	100.0	11177	100.0

Summary

When consideration is given to the age distributions of the two populations, and to the significant difference in degree of urbanization, it is clear that Jews in New York State had a lower rate of first admissions to all hospitals for mental disease than non-Jews. A higher percentage of Jewish first admissions are found in the functional group of psychoses. Contrariwise, a lower percentage of such admissions is found with those disorders of organic origin (i.e., senile psychoses).

REFERENCES

1. For example, Brill, A.A., M.D. and Morris J. Karpas, M.D. Insanity Among Jews. Medical Record. Vol. 86, No. 14. Oct. 1914

2. Malzberg, Benjamin. Prevalence of Mental Disease Among Jews. Mental Hygiene. Vol. 14. Oct. 1930

3. *Ibid.*

4. Malzberg, Benjamin. Mental Disease Among Jews. Mental Hygiene. Vol. 15. Oct. 1931

5. Rosenberg, Louis. Canadian Jews. Canadian Jewish Congress. Montreal. 1939. Page 7.

6. Jewish Communal Survey of Greater New York. First Section. Studies in the New York Jewish Population. Bureau of Jewish Social Research. New York. 1928

7. American Jewish Year Book. Vol. 44 (1942-1943). Jewish Publication Society of America. Philadelphia, 1942. p. 422

8. Robison, Sophia M.(Ed.) Jewish Population Studies. Jewish Social Studies. Publication No. 3. Conference on Jewish Relations. New York, 1943

9. Rosenberg, Louis. Population Characteristics of the Jewish Community of Montreal. Canadian Jewish Population Studies, No. 5. Canadian Jewish Congress. Montreal, 1955. Page 19

10. Rosenberg, Louis. Population Characteristics of Jewish Community of Toronto. Canadian Jewish Population Studies, No. 3. Canadian Jewish Congress. Montreal, 1955. Page 18

11. Malzberg, Benjamin. Social and Biological Aspects of Mental Disease. State Hospitals Press. Utica, N.Y. 1940. Chapter III

12. *See reference* 7. p. 424

13. *See reference* 8.

14. Malzberg, Benjamin. Mental Disease Among Native and Foreign-born White Populations of New York State, 1939-1941. Mental Hygiene. Vol. 39, No. 4. Oct. 1955

PART II

General Paresis

THERE were 197 Jewish first admissions with general paresis to all hospitals for mental disease in New York State during fiscal years 1939-1941, inclusive. They represented 2.8 per cent of all Jewish first admissions. There were 2043 non-Jewish white first admissions with general paresis during the same period, or 5.7 per cent of the corresponding total. Relative to all first admissions, therefore, non-Jews exceeded Jews by 100 per cent in this category of disease. We may also note that Jews represented 16.4 per cent of total white first admissions, but only 8.8 per cent of first admissions with general paresis. Non-Jews, however, who included 83.6 per cent of total white first admissions, included 91.2 per cent of those with general paresis.

It was noted previously that a significantly higher proportion of Jews than of non-Jews were admitted to licensed hospitals for mental disease. In the case of general paresis, however, only 3 per cent of the Jewish first admissions were to licensed hospitals, compared with 5 per cent of non-Jews. Of the Jewish first admissions with general paresis, 70 were native-born, none of whom was admitted to a licensed hospital. Of the native non-Jews, 6.7 per cent were admitted to such hospitals. The low percentage is due, in part, to

TABLE 17—Jewish and non-Jewish white first admissions with general paresis to all hospitals for mental disease in New York State, 1939-1941, classified according to type of hospital and nativity.

	Jews		Non-Jews		Native Jews		Native non-Jews		Foreign-born Jews		Foreign-born non-Jews	
	No.	Per cent	No.	Per cent	No.	Per cent	No.	Per cent	No.	Per cent	No.	Per cent
Civil State hospitals	189	95.9	1910	93.4	69	98.6	1149	91.7	120	94.4	761	96.3
Hospitals for criminal insane	2	1.0	31	1.5	1	1.4	20	1.6	1	0.8	11	1.4
Licensed hospitals	6	3.0	102	5.0	—	—	84	6.7	6	4.7	18	2.3
Total	197	100.0	2043	100.0	70	100.0	1253	100.0	127	100.0	790	100.0

selection by private hospitals with respect to diagnosis. But it is probable that an additional factor is present among Jews. Syphilis, the etiological factor in general paresis, is not distributed randomly in the general population. In addition to selection with respect to age and sex, there is a selection with respect to social status. In general, syphilis is relatively infrequent among Jews, and is more likely to be found among those without strong family ties. Close family attachments frequently influence the choice of type of hospitalization, and the weakening of such affections, or their absence, reduces the probability of application for admission to a private hospital.

Age

Jewish first admissions with general paresis were hospitalized at an average age of 49.8 years. There were only 6 such admissions under age 30, or 3 per cent of the total. Seventy per cent were between 35 and 59 years. The greatest concentration was from 40 to 49 years. There was no significant sex difference, the average ages being 49.8 and 50.0 for males and females, respectively.

TABLE 18—Jewish first admissions with general paresis to all hospitals for mental disease in New York State, 1939-1941, classified according to age.

Age (years)	Number			Per cent		
	Males	Females	Total	Males	Females	Total
20–24	2	—	2	1.4	—	1.0
25–29	1	3	4	0.7	5.9	2.0
30–34	9	3	12	6.2	5.9	6.1
35–39	14	7	21	9.6	13.7	10.7
40–44	29	5	34	19.9	9.8	17.3
45–49	25	7	32	17.1	13.7	16.2
50–54	19	8	27	13.0	15.7	13.7
55–59	19	6	25	13.0	11.8	12.7
60–64	12	7	19	8.2	13.7	9.6
65–69	10	2	12	6.8	3.9	6.1
70–74	4	2	6	2.7	3.9	3.0
75–79	2	1	3	1.4	2.0	1.5
Total	146	51	197	100.0	100.0	100.0

Non-Jewish white first admissions with general paresis were also concentrated within ages 40 to 49, but the general average was only 44.3 years, or 5.5 years less than the average for Jews. Unlike the latter, non-Jewish males were older than non-Jewish females, the averages being 47.4 and 44.3 for males and females, respectively. Both, however, were significantly less than the corresponding ages for Jews.

TABLE 19—Non-Jewish white first admissions with general paresis to all hospitals for mental disease in New York State, 1939-1941, classified according to age.

Age (years)	Number			Per cent		
	Males	Females	Total	Males	Females	Total
5–9	—	1	1	—	0.2	*
10–14	6	1	7	0.4	0.2	0.3
15–19	6	13	19	0.4	2.7	0.9
20–24	5	9	14	0.3	1.8	0.7
25–29	33	27	60	2.1	5.5	2.9
30–34	128	59	187	8.2	12.0	9.2
35–39	218	82	300	14.0	16.7	14.7
40–44	284	80	364	18.3	16.3	17.8
45–49	264	66	330	17.0	13.5	16.2
50–54	254	56	310	16.4	11.4	15.2
55–59	154	40	194	9.9	8.2	9.5
60–64	98	26	124	6.3	5.3	6.1
65–69	63	17	80	4.1	3.5	3.9
70–74	20	8	28	1.3	1.6	1.4
75–79	17	4	21	1.1	0.8	1.0
80–84	3	—	3	0.2	—	0.1
85–89	—	1	1	—	0.2	*
Total	1553	490	2043	100.0	100.0	100.0

*Less than 0.05.

Rates

Table 20 shows average annual rates of first admissions with general paresis. Among Jews, the rates increased to a maximum of 8.0 per 100,000 population at ages 55 to 64. Among non-Jews, the maximum rate, 14.8, was reached at ages 45 to 54. With one exception the rates for non-Jews were in excess at all ages. The average rate for Jews was 3.0 per 100,000, compared with 6.4 for non-Jews.

The Jewish and non-Jewish white populations did not differ radically in their age distributions. Standardizing the rates therefore, did not produce a significant change. Using the total white population of New York State on April 1, 1940, in intervals beginning at age 15, the standardized rates were 3.8 and 8.0 for Jews and non-Jews, respectively.

Environment is a significant factor in the distribution of general paresis. Rates are higher in urban than in rural areas. This affects Jews to a high degree, since they are predominantly urban, with a heavy concentration in New York City. This is reflected in the statistics of first admissions. All Jewish first admissions with general paresis were from urban areas, and only 7.1 per cent were from outside New York City. Of the non-Jewish white

TABLE 20—Jewish and non-Jewish white first admissions with general paresis to all hospitals for mental disease in New York State, 1939-1941, classified according to age and rate per 100,000 population.

Age (years)	Jews					Non-Jews				
	Males	Females	Total No.	Total Per cent	Average annual rate per 100,000	Males	Females	Total No.	Total Per cent	Average annual rate per 100,000
5–9..........	—	—	—	—	—	—	1	1	*	*
10–14........	—	—	—	—	—	6	1	7	0.3	0.3
15–19........	—	—	—	—	—	6	13	19	0.9	0.7
20–24........	2	—	2	1.0	0.3	5	9	14	0.7	0.5
25–34........	10	6	16	8.1	1.3	161	86	247	12.1	4.6
35–44........	43	12	55	27.9	4.8	502	162	664	32.5	13.2
45–54........	44	15	59	30.0	6.4	518	122	640	31.3	14.8
55–64........	31	13	44	22.3	8.0	252	66	318	15.6	11.0
65 and over...	16	5	21	10.7	6.3	103	30	133	6.5	5.6
Total....	146	51	197	100.0	3.0	1553	490	2043	100.0	6.4

*Less than 0.05

TABLE 21—Jewish and non-Jewish white first admissions with general paresis, from New York City, to all hospitals for mental disease in New York State, 1939-1941, classified according to age and rate per 100,000 population.

Age (years)	Jews					Non-Jews				
	Males	Females	Total No.	Total Per cent	Average annual rate per 100,000	Males	Females	Total No.	Total Per cent	Average annual rate per 100,000
5–9..........	—	—	—	—	—	—	—	—	—	—
10–14........	—	—	—	—	—	2	—	2	0.2	0.2
15–19........	—	—	—	—	—	4	10	14	1.3	1.1
20–24........	2	—	2	1.1	0.4	2	4	6	0.5	0.4
25–34........	7	6	13	7.1	1.1	74	47	121	11.0	4.4
35–44........	40	11	51	27.9	4.9	292	80	372	33.8	14.6
45–54........	42	13	55	30.1	6.4	278	59	337	30.6	16.6
55–64........	28	13	41	22.4	8.1	141	30	171	15.5	13.5
65 and over...	16	5	21	11.4	6.9	63	16	79	7.2	8.8
Total....	135	48	183	100.0	3.0	856	246	1102	100.0	7.4

first admissions, 91.6 per cent were from urban areas, and 8.4 per cent were from rural areas. The urban distribution of the non-Jews differed significantly from that for Jews.

The best available comparison is therefore with respect to first admissions from New York City. This is shown in Table 21. Because Jews were primarily from New York City, the average annual rate per 100,000 Jews remained at 3.0, the same as for the State as a whole. The rate for non-Jews however, was 7.4, compared with 6.4 for the State.

Standardizing the rates for New York City in the same manner as for New York State, the rates became 3.9 for Jews and 9.2 for non-Jews. The latter was higher by 135 per cent.

It is therefore clear that general paresis, as measured by rates of first admissions, is less frequent among Jews than among non-Jews. This confirms previous results found for New York State, Massachusetts and Illinois.[1]

Nativity

Of the 197 Jewish first admissions with general paresis, 70, or 35.5 per cent, were born in the United States, and 127, or 64.5 per cent, were foreign-born. This indicates a higher proportion of foreign-born than is true of all Jewish first admissions, and is due primarily to differential age distributions of the two populations. The largest group of the foreign-born was from Russia, with a total of 50. Poland and Austria followed with 23 and 14, respectively. If to these are added native-born of foreign Jewish parentage, we obtain the following: Russia, 74, or 37.6 per cent of the Jewish total with general paresis; Poland, 27, or 13.7 per cent; Austria, 21, or 10.7 per cent; and Germany, 19, or 9.6 per cent; Hungary, 17, or 8.6 per cent; and Roumania, 13, or 7.6 per cent. In the absence of statistics for the corresponding general populations, it is impossible to compute rates of first admissions according to nativity.

TABLE 22—Foreign-born Jewish first admissions with general paresis to all hospitals for mental disease in New York State, 1939–1941, classified according to age and nativity.

Age (years)	Russia			Poland			Austria			Germany			Hungary			Roumania		
	M	F	T	M	F	T	M	F	T	M	F	T	M	F	T	M	F	T
25–29	—	1	1	—	—	—	—	—	—	—	—	—	—	—	—	—	—	—
30–34	2	—	2	—	—	—	—	—	—	—	—	—	—	—	—	—	—	—
35–39	2	1	3	1	—	1	—	1	1	—	—	—	3	—	3	—	1	1
40–44	8	2	10	7	2	9	2	—	2	—	—	—	—	—	—	1	—	1
45–49	5	—	5	4	—	4	1	1	2	3	—	3	—	1	1	3	1	4
50–54	6	3	9	2	2	4	—	1	1	2	—	2	1	—	1	2	—	2
55–59	5	1	6	—	1	1	2	1	3	2	—	2	2	1	3	1	1	2
60–64	7	2	9	—	1	1	1	3	4	—	—	—	—	—	—	1	—	1
65–69	4	—	4	2	—	2	—	—	—	1	—	1	—	1	1	1	—	1
70–74	1	—	1	—	—	—	—	1	1	—	—	—	—	1	1	1	—	1
75–79	—	—	—	—	1	1	—	—	—	—	—	—	—	—	—	—	—	—
Total	40	10	50	16	7	23	6	8	14	8	—	8	6	4	10	10	3	13

TABLE 23—Native Jewish first admissions with general paresis to all hospitals for mental disease in New York State, 1939–1941, classified according to age and nativity of parents.

Age (years)	Russia			Poland			Austria			Germany			Hungary			Roumania		
	M	F	T	M	F	T	M	F	T	M	F	T	M	F	T	M	F	T
20–24	1	—	1	—	—	—	—	—	—	—	—	—	—	—	—	—	—	—
25–29	1	—	1	—	—	—	—	—	—	—	—	—	—	2	2	—	—	—
30–34	3	2	5	1	—	1	1	—	1	—	1	1	1	—	1	1	—	1
35–39	1	1	2	—	1	1	2	1	3	—	—	—	1	—	1	1	—	1
40–44	5	—	5	—	—	—	1	—	1	—	—	—	1	—	1	—	—	—
45–49	4	1	5	—	—	—	1	—	1	—	2	2	1	—	1	—	—	—
50–54	3	—	3	2	—	2	—	1	1	1	—	1	—	—	—	—	—	—
55–59	2	—	2	—	—	—	—	—	—	4	—	4	—	—	—	—	—	—
60–64	—	—	—	—	—	—	—	—	—	1	—	1	1	—	1	—	—	—
65–69	—	—	—	—	—	—	—	—	—	—	1	1	—	—	—	—	—	—
70–74	—	—	—	—	—	—	—	—	—	—	—	—	—	—	—	—	—	—
75–79	—	—	—	—	—	—	—	—	—	1	—	1	—	—	—	—	—	—
Total	20	4	24	3	1	4	5	2	7	7	4	11	5	2	7	2	—	2

Environment

All Jewish first admissions with general paresis were from the urbanized areas of New York State. Of the total Jewish first admissions, 92.9 per cent were from New York City. The remaining 7.1 per cent were from the urbanized fringe surrounding New York City and from up-State cities, such as Buffalo and Rochester. This is in marked contrast to the non-Jewish first admissions, of whom only 53.9 per cent were from New York City, but 37.7 per cent from the remaining urban areas. Rural first admissions with general paresis comprised 8.4 per cent of the non-Jewish first admissions, most of whom were engaged in non-farming pursuits. The foreign-born, whether Jewish or non-Jewish, were concentrated more heavily in New York City than the native-born.

TABLE 24—Jewish and non-Jewish white first admissions with general paresis to all hospitals for mental disease in New York State, 1939-1941, classified according to environment and nativity.

Environment	Jews		Non-Jews		Native Jews		Native non-Jews		Foreign-born Jews		Foreign-born non-Jews	
	No.	Per cent	No.	Per cent	No.	Per cent	No.	Per cent	No.	Per cent	No.	Per cent
Urban	197	100.0	1872	91.6	70	100.0	1101	87.9	127	100.0	771	97.6
New York City	183	92.9	1102	53.9	63	90.0	525	41.9	120	94.5	577	73.0
Other	14	7.1	770	37.7	7	10.0	576	46.0	7	5.5	194	24.6
Rural	—	—	171	8.4	—	—	152	12.1	—	—	19	2.4
Farm	—	—	43	2.1	—	—	39	3.1	—	—	4	0.5
Non-farm	—	—	128	6.3	—	—	113	9.0	—	—	15	1.9
Total	197	100.0	2043	100.0	70	100.0	1253	100.0	127	100.0	790	100.0

Use of alcohol

Of the 197 Jewish first admissions with general paresis, 9, or 4.6 per cent, were intemperate in the use of alcohol. The corresponding percentage for non-Jews was 17.4, almost 4 times as great. Among all first admissions, excluding the alcoholic psychoses, the corresponding percentages were: Jews, 1.9; non-Jews, 12.2. Thus, for both Jews and non-Jews, the percentage of intemperate users of alcohol was greater among general paretics than among all first admissions. Furthermore, the excess ratio was greater among Jews, supporting the previous suggestion that Jewish paretics are of a different social status from Jews in general.

Among foreign-born Jews with general paresis, the percentage of intemperance was 3.9, compared with 17.1 for non-Jews. Both exceeded the corresponding percentages for all foreign-born first admissions (excluding alcoholic psychoses), the excess being greater among Jews.

Among native-born first admissions with general paresis, the percentage of intemperance was 5.7 for Jews and 17.7 for non-Jews. These also are higher than the corresponding percentages for all native first admissions. It appears that native-born Jews had a higher percentage of intemperance than foreign-born Jews.

TABLE 25—Jewish and non-Jewish white first admissions with general paresis to all hospitals for mental disease in New York State, 1939-1941, classified according to use of alcohol and nativity.

Use of alcohol	Jews		Non-Jews		Native Jews		Native non-Jews		Foreign-born Jews		Foreign-born non-Jews	
	No.	Per cent	No.	Per cent	No.	Per cent	No.	Per cent	No.	Per cent	No.	Per cent
Abstinent	114	57.9	674	33.0	38	54.3	441	35.2	76	59.8	233	29.4
Moderate	74	37.6	902	44.2	28	40.5	533	42.5	46	36.2	369	46.7
Intemperate	9	4.6	356	17.4	4	5.7	222	17.7	5	3.9	135	17.1
Unascertained	—	—	111	5.4	—	—	57	4.6	—	—	53	6.7
Total	197	100.0	2043	100.0	70	100.0	1253	100.0	127	100.0	790	100.0

It is evident that Jewish first admissions with general paresis had, in general, lower percentages of intemperate users of alcohol than non-Jews. Both Jews and non-Jews, however, had a higher percentages than all first admissions as a group, indicating an association of alcoholism with general paresis.

In general, it is evident that Jews have a lower incidence of general paresis than non-Jews. The data clearly controvert some statements to the contrary in the early literature, none of which was on a sound statistical basis.[2] There is also a strong association between general paresis and intemperate use of alcohol.

REFERENCES

1. Malzberg, Benjamin. Mental Hygiene. Vol. 14. October 1930, and Vol. 15. October, 1931

2. *See*, for example, Beadles, Cecil F. "The Insane Jew". Journal of Mental Science. Vol. XLVI. October, 1900. No. 195. (New Series, No. 159)

PART III

Alcoholic Psychoses

THERE were 42 Jewish first admissions with alcoholic psychoses to all hospitals for mental disease in New York State during fiscal years 1939-1941, inclusive, or only 0.6 per cent of all Jewish first admissions. There were 2645 non-Jewish white first admissions with such psychoses during the same period, or 7.4 per cent of the corresponding total. The contrast may also be shown as follows. Jews represented 16.4 per cent of total first admissions, but only 1.6 per cent of all first admissions with alcoholic psychoses. Non-Jews, however, represented 83.6 per cent of the total white first admissions, but included 98.4 per cent of those with alcoholic psychoses.

We may also note that only 14.3 per cent of the Jewish alcoholics were admitted to licensed hospitals, in contrast to 24 per cent of all Jewish first admissions. In the case of non-Jewish alcoholics, however, there was a slightly higher percentage of first admissions to the licensed hospitals. The smaller percentage among Jews resulted from the fact that all of the native-born Jews with alcoholic psychoses were admitted to State hospitals. There is a suggestion of social selection in this respect. Jews, in general, place a high valuation upon treatment in private hospitals. More than a fourth of all native Jewish first admissions were to the private hospitals. The fact that none of the native Jews with alcoholic psychoses was so admitted creates the presumption of a different social background among these excessive drinkers.

TABLE 26—Jewish and non-Jewish white first admissions with alcoholic psychoses to all hospitals for mental disease in New York State, 1939-1941, classified according to type of hospital and nativity.

	Jews		Non-Jews		Native Jews		Native non-Jews		Foreign-born Jews		Foreign-born non-Jews	
	No.	Per cent	No.	Per cent	No.	Per cent	No.	Per cent	No.	Per cent	No.	Per cent
Civil State hospitals	36	85.7	2218	83.9	15	100.0	1429	79.8	21	77.8	789	92.4
Hospitals for criminal insane	—	—	19	0.7	—	—	17	0.9	—	—	2	0.2
Licensed hospitals	6	14.3	408	15.4	—	—	345	19.3	6	22.2	63	7.4
Total	42	100.0	2645	100.0	15	100.0	1791	100.0	27	100.0	854	100.0

Age

The average age of Jewish first admissions with alcoholic psychoses was 47.9 years. There were only 3 such cases below age 35. The greatest concentration was at ages 45 to 49. There were only 4 Jewish female first admissions with alcoholic psychoses. Three were aged 35 to 39, and one was in age group 55 to 59.

TABLE 27—Jewish first admissions with alcoholic psychoses to all hospitals for mental disease in New York State, 1939-1941, classified according to age.

Age (years)	Number			Per cent		
	Males	Females	Total	Males	Females	Total
25–29	1	—	1	2.6	—	2.4
30–34	2	—	2	5.3	—	4.8
35–39	4	3	7	10.5	75.0	16.7
40–44	4	—	4	10.5	—	9.5
45–49	11	—	11	28.9	—	26.2
50–54	7	—	7	18.4	—	16.7
55–59	5	1	6	13.2	25.0	14.3
60–64	4	—	4	10.5	—	9.5
Total	38	4	42	100.00	100.0	100.0

TABLE 28—Non-Jewish white first admissions with alcoholic psychoses to all hospitals for mental disease in New York State, 1939-1941, classified according to age.

Age (years)	Number			Per cent		
	Males	Females	Total	Males	Females	Total
20–24	12	2	14	0.5	0.4	0.5
25–29	76	25	101	3.4	5.8	3.8
20–34	199	53	252	9.0	12.3	9.5
35–39	344	56	400	15.5	13.0	15.1
40–44	368	64	432	16.6	14.9	16.3
45–49	374	58	432	16.9	13.4	16.3
50–54	348	66	414	15.7	15.3	15.7
55–59	216	44	260	9.8	10.2	9.8
60–64	153	38	191	6.9	8.8	7.2
65–69	93	14	107	4.2	3.3	4.1
70–74	21	7	28	1.0	1.6	1.1
75–79	9	4	13	0.4	0.9	0.5
80–84	1	—	1	*	—	*
Total	2214	431	2645	100.0	100.0	100.0

*Less than 0.05.

Non-Jewish white first admissions with alcoholic psychoses had an average age of 46.9 years, which did not differ significantly from that for Jews. The admissions were concentrated between ages 35 and 54, this interval including almost two-thirds of the total. The average age at first admission for non-Jewish males, 47.0, did not differ significantly from that for Jewish males, 48.4.

Rate

Table 29 shows the average annual rates of first admissions with alcoholic psychoses among Jews and non-Jews. The average rate was 0.6 per 100,000 Jews. The rates increased from 0.2 at ages 25 to 34 to 1.9 at ages 45 to 54, and 1.8 at ages 55 to 64. The rates among non-Jews were in great excess at all ages. They rose to a maximum of 19.5 per 100,000 at ages 45 to 54. The average rate for non-Jews was 8.3, which exceeded that for Jews in the ratio of 13.8 to 1.

TABLE 29—Jewish and non-Jewish white first admissions with alcoholic psychoses to all hospitals for mental disease in New York State, 1939-1941, classified according to age and rate per 100,000 population.

Age (years)	Jews					Non-Jews				
	Males	Females	Total		Average annual rate per 100,000	Males	Females	Total		Average annual rate per 100,000
			No.	Per cent				No.	Per cent	
20–24	—	—	—	—	—	12	2	14	0.5	0.5
25–34	3	—	3	7.1	0.2	275	78	353	13.3	6.6
35–44	8	3	11	26.2	1.0	712	120	832	31.5	16.5
45–54	18	—	18	42.9	1.9	722	124	846	32.0	19.5
55–64	9	1	10	23.8	1.8	369	82	451	17.1	15.6
65 and over	—	—	—	—	—	124	25	149	5.6	6.3
Total	38	4	42	100.0	0.6	2214	431	2645	100.0	8.3

A further comparison may be made on the basis of standardized rates. The total white population of New York State on April 1, 1940 (in intervals beginning at age 20) was used as standard. On this basis, Jews and non-Jews had standardized rates of 0.9 and 11.7, respectively, the latter being in excess in the ratio of 13 to 1.

A more important correction is with respect to environment. Rates of first admissions with alcoholic psychoses are higher in urban than in rural areas. This affects Jews more than non-Jews. The most significant comparison from this point of view is with respect to New York City.

TABLE 30—Jewish and non-Jewish white first admissions from New York City with alcoholic psychoses to all hospitals for mental disease in New York State, 1939-1941, classified according to age and rate per 100,000 population.

Age (years)	Jews					Non-Jews				
	Males	Females	Total		Average annual rate per 100,000	Males	Females	Total		Average annual rate per 100,000
			No.	Per cent				No.	Per cent	
20–24	—	—	—	—	—	10	2	12	0.7	0.9
25–34	2	—	2	4.9	0.2	169	48	217	12.0	8.0
35–44	8	3	11	26.8	1.0	499	81	580	32.1	22.8
45–54	18	—	18	43.9	2.1	492	86	578	32.0	28.4
55–64	9	1	10	24.4	2.0	264	60	324	17.9	25.6
65 and over	—	—	—	—	—	75	23	98	5.4	10.9
Total	37	4	41	100.0	0.7	1509	300	1809	100.0	12.2

Comparative average annual rates of first admissions from New York City were as follows: Jews, 0.7 per 100,000 population; non-Jews, 12.2 (See Table 30). The rates were also standardized, using the same standard as for New York State. On this basis, the standardized rates were 0.9 for Jews and 16.9 for non-Jews. The latter was in excess in the ratio of 18.8 to 1. It is therefore confirmed once again that Jews have an extraordinarily low rate of alcoholic psychoses.

Nativity

Of the 42 Jewish first admissions with alcoholic psychoses, 15, or 35.7 per cent, were native-born, and 27, or 64.3 per cent, were foreign-born. The proportion of foreign-born is higher than that for the general Jewish population. This results in part from the distribution of the foreign-born about a higher age level, which influences the rate of such admissions.

Of the 27 foreign-born, 11 were from Russia, and 6 from Poland. There were 3 from Austria, and 1 from Hungary. If we define the foreign group as including those of foreign birth, or of foreign parentage, we obtain the following: Russia, 21, and Poland, 7. Together, these two included two-thirds of all Jewish first admissions with alcoholic psychoses. Austria, Germany and Hungary had corresponding totals of 3, 1, and 2.

In the absence of corresponding data for the general Jewish populations of foreign birth or foreign parentage, it is impossible to compute rates of first admissions.

TABLE 31—Foreign-born Jewish first admissions with alcoholic psychoses to all hospitals for mental disease in New York State, 1939–1941, classified according to age and nativity.

Age (years)	Russia			Poland			Austria			Germany			Hungary			Roumania		
	M	F	T	M	F	T	M	F	T	M	F	T	M	F	T	M	F	T
35–39	1	—	1	—	3	3	—	—	—	—	—	—	—	—	—	—	—	—
40–44	—	—	—	—	—	—	—	—	—	—	—	—	—	—	—	—	—	—
45–49	2	—	2	—	—	—	2	—	2	—	—	—	—	—	—	—	—	—
50–54	1	—	1	3	—	3	1	—	1	—	—	—	—	—	—	—	—	—
55–59	4	—	4	—	—	—	—	—	—	—	—	—	—	—	—	—	—	—
60 and over	3	—	3	—	—	—	—	—	—	—	—	—	1	—	1	—	—	—
Total	11	—	11	3	3	6	3	—	3	—	—	—	1	—	1	—	—	—

TABLE 32—Native Jewish first admissions with alcoholic psychoses to all hospitals for mental disease in New York State, 1939–1941, classified according to age and nativity of parents.

Age (years)	Russia			Poland			Austria			Germany			Hungary			Roumania		
	M	F	T	M	F	T	M	F	T	M	F	T	M	F	T	M	F	T
25–29	—	—	—	—	—	—	—	—	—	—	—	—	1	—	1	—	—	—
30–34	1	—	1	—	—	—	—	—	—	—	—	—	—	—	—	—	—	—
35–39	3	—	3	—	—	—	—	—	—	—	—	—	—	—	—	—	—	—
40–44	2	—	2	1	—	1	—	—	—	—	—	—	—	—	—	—	—	—
45–49	2	—	2	—	—	—	—	—	—	1	—	1	—	—	—	—	—	—
50–54	2	—	2	—	—	—	—	—	—	—	—	—	—	—	—	—	—	—
Total	10	—	10	1	—	1	—	—	—	1	—	1	1	—	1	—	—	—

Environment

In 1940, the United States Census Bureau defined the urban inhabitants as those residing in cities or incorporated places with a population of 2500 or more. All others were rural. By this standard, all 42 Jewish first admissions with alcoholic psychoses were from urban areas. In fact, all but 1 were from New York City. The non-Jewish first admissions were also predominantly urban, but on a smaller scale. Thus, 95.1 per cent were urban and 4.9 per cent rural. However, only 68.4 per cent were from New York City compared with 97.6 per cent of the Jewish first admissions.

TABLE 33—Jewish and non-Jewish white first admissions with alcoholic psychoses to all hospitals for mental disease in New York State, 1939-1941, classified according to environment and nativity.

Environment	Jews		Non-Jews		Native Jews		Native non-Jews		Foreign-born Jews		Foreign-born non-Jews	
	No.	Per cent	No.	Per cent	No.	Per cent	No.	Per cent	No.	Per cent	No.	Per cent
Urban	42	100.0	2515	95.1	15	100.0	1679	93.7	27	100.0	836	97.9
New York City	41	97.6	1809	68.4	15	100.0	1096	61.2	26	96.3	713	83.5
Other	1	2.4	706	26.7	—	—	583	32.6	1	3.7	123	14.4
Rural	—	—	130	4.9	—	—	112	6.3	—	—	18	2.1
Farm	—	—	37	1.4	—	—	31	1.7	—	—	6	0.7
Non-farm	—	—	93	3.5	—	—	81	4.6	—	—	12	1.4
Total	42	100.0	2645	100.0	15	100.0	1791	100.0	27	100.0	854	100.0

Summary

As in all previous studies, it is shown that Jews have an exceptionally low rate of alcoholic psychoses. With the rapid acculturation of Jews in the United States it is important to determine whether the process is affecting the statistical level of such psychoses. Unfortunately the statistical enumerations of the Jewish population are not sufficiently accurate to permit a reliable comparison in time.

PART IV

Psychoses with Cerebral Arteriosclerosis

BY 1940, a substantial percentage of the Jewish population was aged 60 years and over. This presented the problem of mental disorders associated with advanced age. One of the two principal groups of such disorders is psychoses with cerebral arteriosclerosis. There were 1134 such first admissions among Jews in New York State during 1939-1941, or 16.2 per cent of the total Jewish first admissions. Only first admissions with dementia praecox exceeded this total. Among non-Jewish first admissions, the corresponding percentage was 18.5. Jews constituted 16.4 per cent of total white first admissions, but 14.7 per cent of the white first admissions with psychoses with cerebral arteriosclerosis. Non-Jews, however, included 83.6 per cent of the total white first admissions, and 85.4 per cent of the arteriosclerotic group. Though not conclusive, these data suggest that psychoses with cerebral arteriosclerosis were less frequent among Jews.

Of all Jewish first admissions, 24 per cent were admitted to licensed hospitals. Of 1134 Jewish first admissions with cerebral arteriosclerosis, only 9.8 per cent were so admitted. This is due, in part, to hesitation by private mental hospitals to accept patients with a poor prognosis. Nevertheless, it is evident that a higher percentage of Jews than of non-Jews were admitted to such hospitals.

TABLE 34—Jewish and non-Jewish first admissions with psychoses with cerebral arteriosclerosis to all hospitals for mental disease in New York State, 1939-1941, classified according to type of hospital and nativity.

	Jews		Non-Jews		Native Jews		Native non-Jews		Foreign-born Jews		Foreign-born non-Jews	
	No.	Per cent	No.	Per cent	No.	Per cent	No.	Per cent	No.	Per cent	No.	Per cent
Civil State hospitals	1022	90.1	6188	93.8	83	82.2	3470	92.3	939	90.9	2718	95.9
Hospitals for criminal insane	1	0.1	14	0.2	—	—	8	0.2	1	0.1	6	0.2
Licensed hospitals	111	9.8	383	6.0	18	17.8	282	7.5	93	9.0	111	3.9
Total	1134	100.0	6595	100.0	101	100.0	3760	100.0	1033	100.0	2835	100.0

TABLE 35—Jewish first admissions with psychoses with cerebral arteriosclerosis to all hospitals for mental disease in New York State, 1939-1941, classified according to age.

Age (years)	Number			Per cent		
	Males	Females	Total	Males	Females	Total
40–44	—	4	4	—	0.6	0.4
45–49	7	13	20	1.4	2.1	1.8
50–54	38	33	71	7.4	5.3	6.3
55–59	76	92	168	14.8	14.8	14.8
60–64	94	124	218	18.4	19.9	19.2
65–69	117	145	262	22.9	23.3	23.1
70–74	91	100	191	17.8	16.1	16.8
75–79	57	78	135	11.1	12.6	11.9
80–84	19	22	41	3.7	3.5	3.6
85–89	9	9	18	1.8	1.4	1.6
90–94	3	2	5	0.6	0.3	0.4
95–99	1	—	1	0.2	—	0.1
Total	512	622	1134	100.0	100.0	100.0

TABLE 36—Non-Jewish white first admissions with psychoses with cerebral arteriosclerosis to all hospitals for mental disease in New York State, 1939-1941, classified according to age.

Age (years)	Number			Per cent		
	Males	Females	Total	Males	Females	Total
35–39	—	6	6	—	0.2	0.1
40–44	14	5	19	0.4	0.2	0.3
45–49	36	43	79	1.0	1.5	1.2
50–54	218	141	359	5.9	4.9	5.4
55–59	405	283	688	11.0	9.8	10.4
60–64	675	536	1211	18.3	18.4	18.4
65–69	811	618	1429	22.0	21.3	21.7
70–74	682	557	1239	18.4	19.2	18.8
75–79	519	443	962	14.0	15.3	14.6
80–84	239	186	425	6.4	6.4	6.4
85–89	74	67	141	2.0	2.3	2.1
90–94	18	15	33	0.5	0.5	0.5
95–99	3	1	4	0.1	*	0.1
Total	3694	2901	6595	100.0	100.0	100.0

*Less than 0.05.

Age

There were few Jewish first admissions with psychoses with cerebral arteriosclerosis under 50 years of age. Three-fourths were between ages 55 and 74. The average age was 66.7 years. There was no significant difference between males and females, the corresponding average ages being 66.8 and 66.6, respectively.

Non-Jewish white first admissions had an average age of 68.3 years, 1.6 years older than Jews. Non-Jewish white males and females had average ages of 68.2 and 68.5 years, respectively. Both exceeded the corresponding average ages for Jews.

Rates

Jews had an average annual rate of 17.1 per 100,000 population compared with 20.6 for the non-Jewish white population. However, this is spurious, arising primarily from variations in the age distributions of the two general populations. At ages 55 to 64, Jews had an average rate of 70.3, compared with 65.8 for non-Jews. At ages 65 and over, Jews had a rate of 197.3, compared with 177.6 for non-Jews.

Previous studies have shown that the rate of first admissions with cerebral arteriosclerosis is higher in an urban than in a rural environment. Because of the concentration of Jews in New York City, a better and more legitimate comparison is made in limiting first admissions to New York City. The resulting comparisons are shown in Table 38. We now find, when degree of urbanization is taken into consideration, that Jews had a lower rate than non-Jews. They were 17.6 for Jews and 25.8 for non-Jews. Only 4 age intervals are available for direct comparison, and in each the average annual rate was lower for Jews. Hence, we conclude that Jews had a significantly lesser frequency of psychoses with cerebral arteriosclerosis than non-Jews.

Nativity

Of the 1134 Jewish first admissions, 101, or 8.9 per cent were native, and 1033, or 91.1 per cent, foreign-born. Sample studies of urban Jewish populations indicated that approximately 35 per cent were foreign-born.[1] It follows, therefore, that the foreign-born exceeded their quota of such psychoses, whereas the native-born had less than their quota. However, this must have resulted from a higher proportion of aged among the foreign-born. In the absence of the necessary data, age-corrected rates of first admissions cannot be computed, and it cannot be concluded, therefore, that foreign-born Jews have a higher rate than native Jews. Such a differential has been established, however, between native and foreign-born white populations as a whole.[2]

Of the 1033 foreign-born Jews, 519, or 50.2 per cent, were born in Russia; 126, or 12.2 per cent, in Poland; and 174, or 16.8 per cent in Austria. The totals for Germany, Hungary and Roumania were 64, 57, and 38, respectively.

TABLE 37—Jewish and non-Jewish white first admissions with psychoses with cerebral arteriosclerosis to all hospitals for mental disease in New York State, 1939-1941, classified according to age and rate per 100,000 population.

Age (years)	Jews					Non-Jews				
	Males	Fe-males	Total No.	Total Per cent	Average annual rate per 100,000	Males	Fe-males	Total No.	Total Per cent	Average annual rate per 100,000
35–44........	—	4	4	0.4	0.4	14	11	25	0.4	0.5
45–54........	45	46	91	8.0	9.8	254	184	438	6.6	10.1
55–64........	170	216	386	34.0	70.3	1080	819	1899	28.8	65.8
65 and over...	297	356	653	57.6	197.3	2346	1887	4233	64.2	177.6
Total....	512	622	1134	100.0	17.1	3694	2901	6595	100.0	20.6

TABLE 38—Jewish and non-Jewish white first admissions with psychoses with cerebral arteriosclerosis, from New York City, to all hospitals for mental disease in New York State, 1939-1941, classified according to age and rate per 100,000 population.

Age (years)	Jews					Non-Jews				
	Males	Fe-males	Total No.	Total Per cent	Average annual rate per 100,000	Males	Fe-males	Total No.	Total Per cent	Average annual rate per 100,000
35–44........	—	4	4	0.4	0.4	7	9	16	0.4	0.6
45–54........	45	44	89	8.3	10.4	163	112	275	7.2	13.5
55–64........	166	205	371	34.6	73.2	709	499	1208	31.6	95.6
65 and over...	273	336	609	56.8	199.5	1280	1040	2320	60.8	258.0
Total....	484	589	1073	100.0	17.6	2159	1660	3819	100.0	25.8

In addition, there were 19 native Jews, whose parents were born in Russia, 12 in Poland, 13 in Austria, and 29 in Germany. The large number with German Jewish parentage is due to the relatively advanced age of this group. The median age was 71 years, significantly higher than for any other group. This is indicative of the fact that German Jews have a relatively long history of immigration to the United States.

TABLE 39—Foreign-born Jewish first adminissions with psychoses with cerebral arteriosclerosis to all hospitals for mental disease in New York State, 1939–1941, classified according to age and nativity.

Age (years)	Russia			Poland			Austria			Germany			Hungary			Roumania		
	M	F	T	M	F	T	M	F	T	M	F	T	M	F	T	M	F	T
40–44	—	1	1	—	—	—	—	—	—	—	—	—	—	—	—	—	—	—
45–49	3	7	10	2	—	2	—	1	1	1	1	2	—	1	1	—	1	1
50–54	16	14	30	3	8	11	5	3	8	—	1	1	—	—	—	2	2	4
55–59	36	50	86	10	11	21	10	15	25	3	3	6	1	5	6	5	1	6
60–64	53	63	116	5	17	22	16	26	42	2	2	4	4	1	5	3	3	6
65–69	46	69	115	14	19	33	18	25	43	7	3	10	8	8	16	3	1	4
70–74	42	38	80	13	7	20	14	16	30	4	11	15	7	6	13	3	6	9
75–79	21	36	57	6	5	11	8	9	17	9	7	16	5	6	11	2	4	6
80–84	4	11	15	2	3	5	6	1	7	—	4	4	3	1	4	2	—	2
85–89	4	3	7	—	1	1	1	—	1	3	1	4	—	1	1	—	—	—
90–94	1	—	1	—	—	—	—	—	—	—	2	2	—	—	—	—	—	—
95–99	1	—	1	—	—	—	—	—	—	—	—	—	—	—	—	—	—	—
Total	227	292	519	55	71	126	78	96	174	29	35	64	28	29	57	20	18	38

TABLE 40—Native Jewish first admissions with psychoses with cerebral arteriosclerosis to all hospitals for mental disease in New York State, 1939–1941, classified according to age and nativity of parents.

Age (years)	Russia			Poland			Austria			Germany			Hungary			Roumania		
	M	F	T	M	F	T	M	F	T	M	F	T	M	F	T	M	F	T
40–44	—	1	1	—	—	—	—	—	—	—	1	1	—	—	—	—	—	—
45–49	—	—	—	1	—	1	—	—	—	—	1	1	—	—	—	—	—	—
50–54	3	1	4	1	—	1	2	1	3	—	1	1	—	1	1	—	—	—
55–59	4	2	6	1	1	2	—	2	2	2	—	2	—	—	—	—	—	—
60–64	4	—	4	1	1	2	1	4	5	1	—	1	—	—	—	—	—	—
65–69	—	2	2	1	—	1	2	—	2	4	4	8	—	—	—	—	—	—
70–74	1	—	1	—	3	3	—	1	1	2	3	5	—	—	—	—	—	—
75–79	—	1	1	1	—	1	—	—	—	4	5	9	—	—	—	—	—	—
80–84	—	—	—	—	—	—	—	—	—	1	—	1	—	—	—	—	—	—
85–89	—	—	—	—	—	—	—	—	—	—	—	—	—	—	—	—	—	—
Total	12	7	19	6	6	12	5	8	13	14	15	29	—	1	1	—	—	—

Environment

Of the 1134 Jewish first admissions, all but 7 were from an urban environment. Of the former, 1073 were from New York City, representing 94.6 per cent of the total. Of the non-Jews, a smaller percentage was urban (88.6), and a larger percentage was rural (11.4). A marked difference is seen in the urban distribution, 57.9 per cent of the non-Jewish first admissions coming from New York City, and 30.7 per cent from the remaining urban areas of the State.

TABLE 41—Jewish and non-Jewish white first admissions with psychoses with cerebral arteriosclerosis to all hospitals for mental disease in New York State, 1939-1941, classified according to environment and nativity.

Environment	Jews		Non-Jews		Native Jews		Native non-Jews		Foreign-born Jews		Foreign-born non-Jews	
	No.	Per cent	No.	Per cent	No.	Per cent	No.	Per cent	No.	Per cent	No.	Per cent
Urban	1127	99.4	5846	88.6	98	97.0	3118	82.9	1029	99.6	2728	96.2
New York City	1073	94.6	3819	57.9	92	91.1	1648	43.8	981	95.0	2171	76.6
Other	54	4.8	2027	30.7	6	5.9	1470	39.1	48	4.6	557	19.6
Rural	7	0.6	749	11.4	3	3.0	642	17.1	4	0.4	107	3.8
Farm	1	0.1	246	3.7	—	—	211	5.6	1	0.1	35	1.2
Non-farm	6	0.5	503	7.6	3	3.0	431	11.4	3	0.3	72	2.5
Total	1134	100.0	6595	100.0	101	100.0	3760	100.0	1033	100.0	2835	100.0

Use of alcohol

Of the 1134 Jewish first admissions, 27, or 2.4 per cent, were intemperate users of alcohol. The corresponding percentage for non-Jews was 12.8, the latter being in excess in the ratio of 5.3 to 1. Among the foreign-born, the percentages of intemperate drinkers were 2.1 for Jews and 14.4 for non-Jews.

TABLE 42—Jewish and non-Jewish white first admissions with psychoses with cerebral arteriosclerosis to all hospitals for mental disease in New York State, 1939-1941, classified according to use of alcohol and nativity.

Use of alcohol	Jews		Non-Jews		Native Jews		Native non-Jews		Foreign-born Jews		Foreign-born non-Jews	
	No.	Per cent	No.	Per cent	No.	Per cent	No.	Per cent	No.	Per cent	No.	Per cent
Abstinent	873	77.0	3372	51.1	75	74.3	2163	57.5	798	77.3	1209	42.6
Moderate	215	19.0	2019	30.6	19	18.8	953	25.3	199	19.3	1063	37.5
Intemperate	27	2.4	841	12.8	5	5.0	431	11.4	22	2.1	410	14.4
Unascertained	19	1.7	363	5.5	2	2.0	213	5.7	14	1.4	153	5.4
Total	1134	100.0	6595	100.0	101	100.0	3760	100.0	1033	100.0	2835	100.0

Of the native Jews, 5.0 per cent were intemperate, compared with 11.4 per cent of the native non-Jews. Though native Jews had a lower percentage than native non-Jews, it may be noted that they had a higher percentage than foreign-born Jews. Native non-Jews had a lower percentage than the foreign-born non-Jews.

Summary

The evidence indicated that psychoses with cerebral arteriosclerosis are less frequent among Jews than among non-Jews.

REFERENCES

1. Robison, Sophia M. (Ed.). Jewish Population Studies. Jewish Social Studies. Publication No. 3. Conference on Jewish Relations. New York. 1943

2. Malzberg, Benjamin. Mental Disease Among Native and Foreign-born White Populations of New York State, 1939-1941. Mental Hygiene. Vol. 39. No. 4. October 1955

PART V

Senile Psychoses

THERE were 530 Jewish first admissions with senile psychoses to all hospitals for mental disease in New York State during 1939-1941, representing 7.6 per cent of all Jewish first admissions. Non-Jewish white first admissions were in significant excess, the senile psychoses including 11.3 per cent of all such admissions. Jewish first admissions with senile psychoses were exceeded in frequency by several of the functional groups of mental disorders, and by psychoses with cerebral arteriosclerosis. Among non-Jews, the senile psychoses included the third largest total. Jews represented 16.4 per cent of total white first admissions, but only 11.7 per cent of those with senile psychoses. For white non-Jews the corresponding percentages were 83.6 and 88.3, respectively. This suggests a higher frequency of senile psychoses among non-Jews.

TABLE 43—Jewish and non-Jewish white first admissions with senile psychoses to all hospitals for mental disease in New York State, 1939-1941, classified according to type of hospital and nativity.

	Jews		Non-Jews		Native Jews		Native non-Jews		Foreign-born Jews		Foreign-born non-Jews	
	No.	Per cent	No.	Per cent	No.	Per cent	No.	Per cent	No.	Per cent	No.	Per cent
Civil State hospitals	474	89.4	3831	95.3	37	75.6	2125	94.1	437	90.9	1706	96.9
Hospitals for criminal insane	2	0.4	5.	0.1	—	—	2	0.1	2	0.4	3	0.2
Licensed hospitals	54	10.2	183	4.6	12	24.4	132	5.8	42	8.7	51	2.9
Total	530	100.0	4019	100.0	49	100.0	2259	100.0	481	100.0	1760	100.0

Because of the poor prognosis for senile disorder, licensed (private) hospitals do not readily accept such cases. It is of interest, nevertheless, that 54 of the Jewish senile first admissions, or 10.2 per cent, were admitted to licensed hospitals, compared with only 4.6 per cent of the non-Jewish admissions. The contrast is even greater among the native-born, for whom the corresponding percentages were 24.4 and 5.8, respectively. For the foreign-born, they were 8.7 and 2.9 per cent for Jews and non-Jews, respectively. The choice of hospital is probably influenced in part by the characteristic respect of Jews, in general, for the private practitioner and private medical facilities. It is also due, however, to close family relations among Jews, which impels younger people to assume larger responsibilities for the care of elderly relatives.

Age

The average age of Jewish first admissions with senile psychoses was 75.9 years. Two-thirds were from 70 to 84 years old. The difference between males and females was not significant, the average ages being 76.3 and 75.6 for males and females, respectively.

The non-Jewish white first admissions were significantly older. Their average age was 77.2 years. Males and females had average ages of 77.2 and 77.1, respectively. Both exceeded the corresponding ages for Jews.

Rates

Jews had an average annual rate of first admissions with senile psychoses of 8.0 per 100,000, compared with 12.6 for non-Jews. In the statistics of the general Jewish population, all aged 65 and over were grouped together. This age interval included over 90 per cent of the first admissions with senile psychoses among both Jews and non-Jews. It is therefore impossible to standardize the rates of first admissions. Direct comparison shows that there was little difference in age specific rates under age 65. At the higher age interval, however, Jews and non-Jews had rates of 145.9 and 158.4, respectively.

Because of the concentration of Jews in New York City, in contrast to the greater dispersion of non-Jews, it is necessary to consider the degree of urbanization. As with other groups of mental disorders, the comparison is best limited to first admissions from New York City. Ninety-four per cent of the Jewish first admissions with senile psychoses were from New York City. They provided an average annual rate of 8.2 per 100,000 Jews. Non-Jewish whites from New York City had an average annual rate of 13.8. At ages 55 to 64, the rates were 7.9 and 9.0 for Jews and non-Jews, respectively. At ages 65 and over, the rates were 148.7 and 214.2 for Jews and non-Jews, respectively. It may therefore be inferred that Jews have a lesser frequency of senile psychoses than non-Jews.

Nativity

Of the 530 Jewish first admissions with senile psychoses, 49, or 9.2 per cent, were native, and 481, or 90.8 per cent, were foreign-born. Since the foreign-born constitute 35 per cent of the urban Jewish population, it appears that they exceeded their expected quota of senile first admissions. Without additional data, it cannot be affirmed that foreign-born Jews have a higher rate

TABLE 44—Jewish first admissions with senile psychoses to all hospitals for mental disease in New York State, 1939-1941, classified according to age.

Age (years)	Number			Per cent		
	Males	Females	Total	Males	Females	Total
40–44	1	—	1	0.6	—	0.2
45–49	—	3	3	—	0.8	0.6
50–54	2	—	2	1.1	—	0.4
55–59	4	4	8	2.3	1.1	1.5
60–64	6	27	33	3.4	7.6	6.2
65–69	16	49	65	9.2	13.8	12.3
70–74	39	85	124	22.4	23.9	23.4
75–79	50	82	132	28.7	23.0	24.9
80–84	36	67	103	20.7	18.8	19.4
85–89	17	23	40	9.8	6.4	7.5
90–94	2	13	15	1.1	3.7	2.8
95–99	—	3	3	—	0.8	0.6
100–104	1	—	1	0.6	—	0.2
Total	174	356	530	100.0	100.0	100.0

TABLE 45—Non-Jewish white first admissions with senile psychoses to all hospitals for mental disease in New York State, 1939-1941, classified according to age.

Age (years)	Number			Per cent		
	Males	Females	Total	Males	Females	Total
50–54	6	15	21	0.4	0.7	0.5
55–59	13	24	37	0.8	1.0	0.9
60–64	77	109	186	4.5	4.7	4.6
65–69	154	270	424	9.0	11.7	10.6
70–74	365	452	817	21.4	19.5	20.3
75–79	466	567	1033	27.4	24.4	25.7
80–84	406	529	935	23.9	22.8	23.3
85–89	168	272	440	9.9	11.7	11.0
90–94	41	69	110	2.4	3.0	2.7
95–99	5	9	14	0.3	0.4	0.3
100–104	1	1	2	0.1	*	*
Total	1702	2317	4019	100.0	100.0	100.0

*Less than 0.05

TABLE 46—Jewish and non-Jewish white first admissions with senile psychoses to all hospitals for mental disease in New York State, 1939-1941, classified according to age and rate per 100,000 population.

Age (years)	Jews					Non-Jews				
	Males	Females	Total		Average annual rate per 100,000	Males	Females	Total		Average annual rate per 100,000
			No.	Per cent				No.	Per cent	
35–44........	1	—	1	0.2	0.1	—	—	—	—	—
45–54........	2	3	5	0.9	0.5	6	15	21	0.5	0.4
55–64........	10	31	41	7.7	7.4	90	133	223	5.5	7.7
65 and over...	161	322	483	91.1	145.9	1606	2169	3775	93.9	158.4
Total....	174	356	530	100.0	8.0	1702	2317	4019	100.0	12.6

TABLE 47—Jewish and non-Jewish white first admissions with senile psychoses, from New York City, to all hospitals for mental disease in New York State, 1939-1941, classified according to age and rate per 100,000 population.

Age (years)	Jews					Non-Jews				
	Males	Females	Total		Average annual rate per 100,000	Males	Females	Total		Average annual rate per 100,000
			No.	Per cent				No.	Per cent	
35–44........	1	—	1	0.2	0.1	—	—	—	—	—
45–54........	2	3	5	1.0	0.6	1	4	5	0.2	0.2
55–64........	10	30	40	8.0	7.9	44	70	114	5.6	9.0
65 and over...	148	306	454	90.8	148.7	812	1114	1926	94.2	214.2
Total....	161	339	500	100.0	8.2	857	1188	2045	100.0	13.8

of first admissions with senile psychoses than native Jews. This has been shown to be true of the total white population of New York State, and suggests by analogy, that it may also be true of Jews.

By far the largest foreign-born group was of Russian nativity. They constituted 47 per cent of all Jewish first admissions with senile psychoses. Whether their rate of first admissions is equally high cannot be determined until all necessary data become available (i.e., complete age statistics). No other group of foreign-born Jewish first admissions equaled the Russian in number. Poland, Austria and Germany were the birthplaces of 57, 71, and 43 first admissions, respectively.

TABLE 48—Foreign-born Jewish first admissions with senile psychoses to all hospitals for mental disease in New York State, 1939–1941, classified according to age and nativity.

Age (years)	Russia			Poland			Austria			Germany			Hungary			Roumania		
	M	F	T	M	F	T	M	F	T	M	F	T	M	F	T	M	F	T
40–44	1	—	1	—	—	—	—	—	—	—	—	—	—	—	—	—	—	—
45–49	—	—	—	—	3	3	—	—	—	—	—	—	—	—	—	—	—	—
50–54	—	—	—	—	—	—	—	—	—	—	—	—	1	—	1	—	—	—
55–59	—	—	—	—	—	—	—	—	—	—	—	—	1	—	1	—	1	1
60–64	1	14	15	2	2	4	—	6	6	—	1	1	—	2	2	2	1	3
65–69	9	26	35	—	1	1	4	10	14	1	2	3	2	1	3	—	1	1
70–74	21	42	63	4	14	18	5	10	15	2	4	6	1	4	5	—	4	4
75–79	30	36	66	6	11	17	2	9	11	5	8	13	1	2	3	—	—	—
80–84	13	22	35	6	6	12	6	10	16	2	12	14	—	3	3	3	4	7
85–89	12	9	21	—	1	1	2	5	7	1	4	5	1	—	1	—	1	1
90–94	2	8	10	—	1	1	—	1	1	—	1	1	—	—	—	—	2	2
95–99	—	2	2	—	—	—	—	—	—	—	—	—	—	—	—	—	—	—
100–104	—	—	—	—	—	—	1	—	1	—	—	—	—	—	—	—	—	—
Total	89	159	248	18	39	57	20	51	71	11	32	43	7	12	19	5	14	19

TABLE 49—Native Jewish first admissions with senile psychoses to all hospitals for mental disease in New York State, 1939–1941, classified according to age and nativity of parents.

Age (years)	Russia			Poland			Austria			Germany			Hungary			Roumania		
	M	F	T	M	F	T	M	F	T	M	F	T	M	F	T	M	F	T
50–54	—	—	—	—	—	—	—	—	—	1	—	1	—	—	—	—	—	—
55–59	—	—	—	—	—	—	—	—	—	—	—	—	—	—	—	—	—	—
60–64	—	—	—	—	—	—	—	—	—	—	—	—	—	—	—	—	—	—
65–69	—	—	—	—	—	—	—	—	—	—	2	2	—	—	—	—	—	—
70–74	—	—	—	1	—	1	—	—	—	2	1	3	—	—	—	—	—	—
75–79	—	2	2	—	—	—	—	—	—	3	9	12	1	—	1	—	—	—
80–84	—	—	—	—	—	—	—	—	—	4	3	7	—	1	1	—	—	—
85–89	—	—	—	—	—	—	—	—	—	1	2	3	—	—	—	—	—	—
Total	—	2	2	1	—	1	—	—	—	11	17	28	1	1	2	—	—	—

Of the native-born Jewish first admissions, only those with German-born parents were of a substantial number. This is clearly associated with the longer history of German Jews in the United States.

Environment

Of the Jewish first admissions with senile psychoses, all but 2 were from urban areas. Of the urban group, 500 were from New York City, and only 28 from other urban areas of New York State. In contrast, 88 per cent of the non-Jewish white first admissions were from urban areas, and 12 per cent from rural areas. In contrast to the few Jews who inhabited urban areas outside New York City, 37 per cent of the non-Jews came from such areas.

TABLE 50—Jewish and non-Jewish white first admissions with senile psychoses to all hospitals for mental disease in New York State, 1939-1941, classified according to environment and nativity.

Environment	Jews		Non-Jews		Native Jews		Native non-Jews		Foreign-born Jews		Foreign-born non-Jews	
	No.	Per cent	No.	Per cent	No.	Per cent	No.	Per cent	No.	Per cent	No.	Per cent
Urban	528	99.6	3535	88.0	48	98.0	1880	83.2	480	99.8	1655	94.0
New York City	500	94.3	2045	50.9	44	89.8	860	38.1	456	94.8	1185	67.3
Other	28	5.3	1490	37.1	4	8.2	1020	45.2	24	5.0	470	26.7
Rural	2	0.4	484	12.0	1	2.0	379	16.8	1	0.2	105	6.0
Farm	—	—	122	3.0	—	—	98	4.3	—	—	24	1.4
Non-farm	2	0.4	362	9.0	1	2.0	281	12.4	1	0.2	81	4.6
Total	530	100.0	4019	100.0	49	100.0	2259	100.0	481	100.0	1760	100.0

TABLE 51—Jewish and non-Jewish white first admissions with senile psychoses to all hospitals for mental disease in New York State, 1939-1941, classified according to use of alcohol and nativity.

Use of alcohol	Jews		Non-Jews		Native Jews		Native non-Jews		Foreign-born Jews		Foreign-born non-Jews	
	No.	Per cent	No.	Per cent	No.	Per cent	No.	Per cent	No.	Per cent	No.	Per cent
Abstinent	424	80.0	2491	62.0	36	73.4	1510	66.8	391	81.3	978	55.6
Moderate	81	15.3	991	24.7	13	26.5	434	19.2	68	14.1	557	31.6
Intemperate	13	2.4	277	6.9	—	—	154	6.8	10	2.1	126	7.2
Unascertained	12	2.3	260	6.4	—	—	161	7.1	12	2.5	99	5.6
Total	530	100.0	4019	100.0	49	100.0	2259	100.0	481	100.0	1760	100.0

Use of alcohol

Of the Jewish first admissions with senile psychoses, 13, or 2.4 per cent, were intemperate users of alcohol, compared with 6.9 per cent of the non-Jews. None of the native Jewish first admissions with such disorders was intemperate, compared with 6.8 per cent of the native non-Jews. Among the foreign-born, the corresponding percentages were 2.1 for Jews and 7.2 for non-Jews.

Compared to all first admissions, exclusive of alcoholic psychoses, Jewish first admissions with senile psychoses had a higher percentage of intemperate drinkers. This was noted especially among the foreign-born.

Summary

The available data point to a lesser incidence of senile psychoses among Jews than among non-Jews.

PART VI

Involutional Psychoses

OF the 6987 Jewish first admissions during 1939-1941, inclusive 621, or 8.9 per cent, were involutional psychoses. Non-Jewish white first admissions with such psychoses totaled 2286, or 6.4 per cent of all first admissions. Another comparison shows that Jews represented 21.3 per cent of first admissions with involutional psychoses, in contrast to 16.4 per cent of all first admissions. Non-Jews, on the other hand, represented 78.6 per cent of all first admissions with involutional psychoses, as against 83.6 per cent of all first admissions. Jews exceeded their expected quota by 30 per cent. Non-Jews reached only 94 per cent of their expectation. This suggests a higher frequency of involutional psychoses among Jews.

Table 52 shows for both Jews and non-Jews, a higher percentage of admissions to licensed hospitals than occurred among mental disorders of organic origin, such as senile or arteriosclerotic. This is due in large part to selection by private hospitals of types of patients they deem suitable for treatment. It is also evident that Jews send a larger percentage of patients with involutional disorders to licensed hospitals than do non-Jews.

TABLE 52—Jewish and non-Jewish white first admissions with involutional psychoses to all hospitals for mental disease in New York State, 1939-1941, classified according to type of hospital and nativity.

	Jews		Non-Jews		Native Jews		Native non-Jews		Foreign-born Jews		Foreign-born non-Jews	
	No.	Per cent	No.	Per cent	No.	Per cent	No.	Per cent	No.	Per cent	No.	Per cent
Civil State hospitals	474	76.3	1851	81.0	91	73.4	1055	76.5	383	77.1	796	87.8
Hospitals for criminal insane	—	—	9	0.4	—	—	3	0.2	—	—	6	0.7
Licensed hospitals	147	23.7	426	18.6	33	26.6	321	23.3	144	22.9	105	11.6
Total	621	100.0	2286	100.0	124	100.0	1379	100.0	497	100.0	907	100.0

Age

The average age of Jewish first admissions with involutional psychoses was 51.9 years. There were only 6 such cases under 40 years of age. More than three-fourths were between 45 and 59 years. Males and females had averages of 52.9 and 51.5 years, respectively, the difference being statistically significant.

Non-Jewish white first admissions had an average age of 52.4 years. Males and females had average ages of 52.9 and 51.5 years, respectively.

TABLE 53—Jewish first admissions with involutional psychoses to all hospitals for mental disease in New York State, 1939-1941, classified according to age.

Age (years)	Number			Per cent		
	Males	Females	Total	Males	Females	Total
35–39	1	5	6	0.6	1.1	1.0
40–44	12	61	73	7.6	13.2	11.8
45–49	36	128	164	22.8	27.6	26.4
50–54	56	142	198	35.4	30.7	31.9
55–59	37	85	122	23.4	18.4	19.6
60–64	12	39	51	7.6	8.4	8.2
65–69	1	3	4	0.6	0.6	0.6
70–74	3	—	3	1.9	—	0.4
Total	158	463	621	100.0	100.0	100.0

TABLE 54—Non-Jewish white first admissions with involutional psychoses to all hospitals for mental disease in New York State, 1939-1941, classified according to age.

Age (years)	Number			Per cent		
	Males	Females	Total	Males	Females	Total
25–29	—	1	1	—	0.1	*
30–34	—	2	2	—	0.1	0.1
35–39	4	27	31	0.6	1.7	1.4
40–44	63	228	291	8.9	14.4	12.7
45–49	122	441	563	17.2	28.0	24.6
50–54	215	446	661	30.3	28.3	28.9
55–59	171	262	433	24.1	16.6	18.9
60–64	77	107	184	10.8	6.8	8.1
65–69	51	48	99	7.2	3.0	4.3
70–74	5	14	19	0.7	0.9	0.8
75–79	2	—	2	0.3	—	0.1
Total	710	1576	2286	100.0	100.0	100.0

*Less than 0.05.

Rate

The average annual rate of first admissions increased among Jews from 6.9 per 100,000 at ages 35 to 44 to 39.1 at ages 45 to 54, and decreased to 31.4 at ages 55 to 64. These rates were in excess of the corresponding rates among non-Jews. The average annual rate was 9.4 per 100,000 Jews and 7.1 per 100,000 non-Jews.

TABLE 55 Jewish and non-Jewish white first admissions with involutional psychoses to all hospitals for mental disease in New York State, 1939-1941, classified according to age and rate per 100,000 population.

Age (years)	Jews					Non-Jews				
	Males	Females	Total No.	Total Per cent	Average annual rate per 100,000	Males	Females	Total No.	Total Per cent	Average annual rate per 100,000
25–34	—	—	—	—	—	—	3	3	0.1	0.1
35–44	13	66	79	12.7	6.9	67	255	322	14.1	6.4
45–54	92	270	362	58.3	39.1	337	887	1224	53.5	28.2
55–64	49	124	173	27.9	31.4	248	369	617	27.0	21.4
65 and over	4	3	7	1.1	2.1	58	62	120	5.3	5.0
Total	158	463	621	100.0	9.4	710	1576	2286	100.0	7.1

TABLE 56—Jewish and non-Jewish white first admissions with involutional psychoses, from New York City, to all hospitals for mental disease in New York State, 1939-1941, classified according to age and rate per 100,000 population.

Age (years)	Jews					Non-Jews				
	Males	Females	Total No.	Total Per cent	Average annual rate per 100,000	Males	Females	Total No.	Total Per cent	Average annual rate per 100,000
25–34	—	—	—	—	—	—	1	1	0.1	*
35–44	13	62	75	13.2	7.1	46	169	215	15.9	8.4
45–54	84	252	336	59.1	39.3	224	536	760	56.4	37.4
55–64	39	112	151	26.5	29.8	128	203	331	24.6	26.2
65 and over	4	3	7	1.2	2.3	15	26	41	3.0	4.6
Total	140	429	569	100.0	9.3	413	935	1348	100.0	9.1

*Less than 0.05.

For reasons expressed previously, it is desirable to limit the comparisons to New York City. The results are shown in Table 56. At ages 35 to 44, the average annual rate for Jews was less than that for non-Jews. Between ages 45 to 64, the rates for Jews were somewhat higher. The average rates per 100,000 were 9.3 and 9.1 for Jews and non-Jews, respectively. If we limit the comparison to ages 35 and over, and use as a base the white population of New York State as of April 1, 1940, of corresponding age, the rates become 20.4 for Jews, and 20.0 for non-Jews. The original estimate of the Jewish population was clearly an underestimate. Therefore, any correction would necessarily decrease the rate for Jews, and at the same time increase that for non-Jews. It must be concluded that for all practical purposes, the rates for Jews and non-Jews with reference to involutional psychoses must be considered equal.

Nativity

Of the 621 Jewish first admissions, 124, or 20 per cent, were native and 497, or 80 per cent, were foreign-born. Of all Jewish first admissions, only 55 per cent were foreign-born. Both are in excess of the proportion of foreign-born Jews in the urban population of New York State. It is probable, therefore, that foreign-born Jews have a higher rate of first admissions with involutional psychoses than native-born, though in the absence of complete age statistics this cannot be verified. For the white population as a whole, it has been shown that the rate is higher for the foreign-born.

Of the 497 foreign-born Jews, 245, or 49.3 per cent, were born in Russia. No other group was of comparable numerical importance. There were 93 who were born in Poland, 73 in Austria, 30 in Hungary, and 11 in Roumania. Only 8 were born in Germany.

It is of statistical importance to compare natives of foreign parentage with the corresponding groups of foreign-born. Unfortunately, the data for a complete analysis are not available. But it is interesting to note a total of 42 Jewish first admissions of Russian parentage, compared with only 20 of German parentage. This may be due to the fact that Jews of Russian origin are a more recent immigrant group, and are therefore younger and more likely to be in the age range associated with involutional disorder.

Environment

Of the Jewish first admissions, 615, or 99 per cent, were from urban areas. There was a further concentration in New York City, which included 569, or 91.6 per cent of the total. The non-Jews were also predominantly urban, but not to the same degree as Jews. Furthermore, only 59.0 per cent were from New York City, compared to 91.6 per cent for Jews. On the other hand, 32.5 per cent were from other urban areas, in contrast to only 7.4 per cent for Jews.

TABLE 57—Foreign-born Jewish first admissions with involutional psychoses to all hospitals for mental disease in New York State, 1939–1941, classified according to age and nativity.

Age (years)	Russia			Poland			Austria			Germany			Hungary			Roumania		
	M	F	T	M	F	T	M	F	T	M	F	T	M	F	T	M	F	T
35–39	—	—	—	1	1	2	—	1	1	—	—	—	—	—	—	—	—	—
40–44	4	22	26	—	13	13	1	3	4	2	—	2	—	5	5	—	1	1
45–49	12	48	60	11	14	25	6	15	21	—	—	—	—	10	10	1	3	4
50–54	22	57	79	12	23	35	6	15	21	—	1	1	—	6	6	4	8	12
55–59	13	37	50	3	10	13	5	14	19	1	3	4	5	2	7	—	—	—
60–64	6	19	25	—	5	5	1	6	7	—	1	1	—	1	1	—	—	—
65–69	—	2	2	—	—	—	—	—	—	—	—	—	1	—	1	—	—	—
70–74	3	—	3	—	—	—	—	—	—	—	—	—	—	—	—	—	—	—
Total	60	185	245	27	66	93	19	54	73	3	5	8	6	24	30	5	12	17

TABLE 58—Native Jewish first admissions with involutional psychoses to all hospitals for mental disease in New York State, 1939–1941, classified according to age and nativity of parents.

Age (years)	Russia			Poland			Austria			Germany			Hungary			Roumania		
	M	F	T	M	F	T	M	F	T	M	F	T	M	F	T	M	F	T
35–39	—	1	1	—	—	—	—	—	—	—	—	—	—	—	—	—	—	—
40–44	2	7	9	—	1	1	1	2	3	—	2	2	—	—	—	1	—	1
45–49	2	15	17	1	3	4	—	6	6	1	—	1	1	—	1	—	1	1
50–54	2	5	7	3	2	5	1	2	3	1	4	4	—	3	3	—	—	—
55–59	1	4	5	3	—	3	3	3	6	2	5	7	—	1	1	—	1	1
60–64	3	—	3	—	—	—	—	3	3	1	3	4	—	—	—	—	—	—
65–69	—	—	—	—	—	—	—	—	—	—	1	1	—	—	—	—	—	—
Total	10	32	42	7	6	13	5	16	21	5	15	20	1	4	5	1	2	3

TABLE 59—Jewish and non-Jewish white first admissions with involutional psychoses to all hospitals for mental disease in New York State, 1939-1941, classified according to environment and nativity.

Environment	Jews		Non-Jews		Native Jews		Native non-Jews		Foreign-born Jews		Foreign-born non-Jews	
	No.	Per cent	No.	Per cent	No.	Per cent	No.	Per cent	No.	Per cent	No.	Per cent
Urban	615	99.0	2092	91.5	123	99.2	1212	87.9	492	99.0	880	97.0
New York City	569	91.6	1348	59.0	104	83.9	675	49.0	465	93.6	673	74.2
Other	46	7.4	744	32.5	19	15.3	537	38.9	27	5.4	207	22.8
Rural	6	1.0	194	8.5	1	0.8	167	12.1	5	1.0	27	3.0
Farm	—	—	52	2.3	—	—	47	3.4	—	—	5	0.6
Non-farm	6	1.0	142	6.2	1	0.8	120	8.7	5	1.0	22	2.4
Total	621	100.0	2286	100.0	124	100.0	1379	100.0	497	100.0	907	100.0

Use of Alcohol

Only 8 of the 621 Jewish first admissions with involutional psychoses, or 1.3 per cent, were classified as intemperate users of alcohol. In contrast, non-Jews included 6.3 per cent in this category. Both Jews and non-Jews had lower percentages of intemperance than corresponding groups of total first admissions, exclusive of alcoholic psychoses.

Of the foreign-born Jews, 1 per cent were intemperate users of alcohol, compared to 2.4 per cent of native Jews.

TABLE 60—Jewish and non-Jewish white first admissions with involutional psychoses to all hospitals for mental disease in New York State, 1939-1941, classified according to use of alcohol and nativity.

Use of alcohol	Jews		Non-Jews		Native Jews		Native non-Jews		Foreign-born Jews		Foreign-born non-Jews	
	No.	Per cent	No.	Per cent	No.	Per cent	No.	Per cent	No.	Per cent	No.	Per cent
Abstinent	511	82.3	1353	59.2	99	79.8	821	59.5	412	82.9	532	58.7
Moderate	85	13.7	695	30.4	20	16.1	413	29.9	65	13.1	282	31.1
Intemperate	8	1.3	144	6.3	3	2.4	82	5.9	5	1.0	62	6.8
Unascertained	17	2.7	94	4.1	2	1.6	63	4.6	15	3.0	31	3.4
Total	621	100.0	2286	100.0	124	100.0	1379	100.0	497	100.0	907	100.0

Summary

When differential distributions with respect to environment and age were given due consideration, it seemed clear that there was no significant difference in rates of first admissions with involutional psychoses between Jews and non-Jews.

PART VII

Manic-depressive Psychoses

THERE were 854 Jewish first admissions with manic-depressive psychoses to all hospitals for mental disease in New York State during fiscal years, 1939-1941, or 12.2 per cent of all Jewish first admissions. The corresponding percentage for non-Jews was 7.1. These disorders were the third largest category among Jews, but only fifth in numerical order among non-Jews. Of the total white first admissions with manic-depressive psychoses, Jews included 25.2 per cent, non-Jews 74.8 per cent. Of the total first admissions (all psychoses), Jews represented 16.4 per cent, non-Jews 83.6 per cent. Jews were therefore over-represented among first admissions with manic-depressive psychoses.

It was shown previously that 24 per cent of all Jewish first admissions were to licensed mental hospitals, compared with only 13.2 per cent of non-Jews. For the manic-depressive psychoses, however, the corresponding percentages were 53.4 for Jews and 26.4 for non-Jews. It will be shown in a subsequent section, that only first admissions with psychoneuroses have a higher percentage of admissions to licensed hospitals than those with manic-depressive psychoses. Other studies have shown that Jews have a generally enlightened attitude towards the significance of "functional" mental disorders, seek treatment readily, and attach special value to private as opposed to public facilities for treatment.[1]

TABLE 61—Jewish and non-Jewish white first admissions with manic-depressive psychoses to all hospitals for mental disease in New York State, 1939-1941, classified according to type of hospital and nativity.

	Jews		Non-Jews		Native Jews		Native non-Jews		Foreign-born Jews		Foreign-born non-Jews	
	No.	Per cent	No.	Per cent	No.	Per cent	No.	Per cent	No.	Per cent	No.	Per cent
Civil State hospitals	396	46.4	1854	73.3	240	48.5	1426	72.8	156	43.4	428	75.0
Hospitals for criminal insane	2	0.2	8	0.3	—	—	6	0.3	2	0.6	2	0.3
Licensed hospitals	456	53.4	669	26.4	255	51.5	528	26.9	201	56.0	141	24.7
Total	854	100.0	2531	100.0	495	100.0	1960	100.0	359	100.0	571	100.0

Age

Jewish first admissions with manic-depressive psychoses had an average age of 38.0 years. Seventy per cent were between ages 25 and 49. Males had an average age of 39.0 years, females, 37.6, but the difference is not statistically significant.

Non-Jewish white first admissions had an average age of 39.4 years, significantly greater than that for Jews. Non-Jewish males had a significantly higher average age than non-Jewish females, these being 41.3 and 38.4, respectively. Non-Jewish males and females each had a higher average age than Jews, though the difference is not significant for females.

Rates

Average annual rates of first admissions with manic-depressive psychoses rose among Jews from 0.2 per 100,000 population at ages 10 to 14 to a maximum of 22.9 at ages 35 to 44. Non-Jews had a similar trend, though at lower levels. They reached a maximum rate of 13.4 at ages 35 to 44. The average rate was 12.9 for Jews and 7.9 for non-Jews. Age specific rates were higher for Jews throughout the age range. Hence, the standardized rate for Jews, 15.6, was higher than that for non-Jews, 10.0. The standard population was the same as that used for all first admissions (See Section I).

The chief difficulty rests with differences in urban-rural distribution of population. Urban rates are higher and hence affect Jews more than non-Jews, since the former are concentrated almost completely in New York City. Rates of first admission were therefore computed for New York City. Since the bulk of the Jewish population and the Jewish first admissions was from New York City, the results did not vary greatly from those for the entire State. There were some differences for non-Jews, the rates increasing at all ages under 45. Nevertheless, rates for Jews remained in excess, throughout the age range. The average rates were 12.3 for Jews and 8.1 for non-Jews.

The rates were again standardized, and became 14.8 for Jews and 9.8 for non-Jews. The rate for Jews was too high, because the general Jewish population was undoubtedly overestimated. But with an error of 10 per cent, a correction on this basis would still leave the rate for Jews significantly in excess of that for non-Jews. Hence, we may conclude that the relative frequency of manic-depressive psychoses is greater for Jews than for non-Jews.

Nativity

Of the 854 Jewish first admissions with manic-depressive psychoses, 495, or 58.0 per cent, were native, and 359, or 42.0 per cent, were foreign-born. The foreign-born Jewish population was estimated to represent 35 per cent of the Jewish population. They therefore had more than their expected quota of the first admissions whereas the native Jews had less than their expectation. It cannot be inferred, however, that foreign-born Jews had a higher rate of such psychoses, because this depends upon the age distribution of the corresponding general population. The complete age statistics

TABLE 62—Jewish first admissions with manic-depressive psychoses to all hospitals for mental disease in New York State, 1939-1941, classified according to age.

Age (years)	Number			Per cent		
	Males	Females	Total	Males	Females	Total
10–14	—	1	1	—	0.2	0.1
15–19	17	27	44	7.2	4.4	5.2
20–24	16	67	83	6.7	10.9	9.7
25–29	29	84	113	12.2	13.6	13.2
30–34	35	86	121	14.7	14.0	14.2
35–39	25	116	141	10.5	18.8	16.5
40–44	45	75	120	18.9	12.2	14.1
45–49	22	77	99	9.2	12.5	11.6
50–54	27	34	61	11.3	5.5	7.1
55–59	9	21	30	3.8	3.4	3.5
60–64	7	15	22	2.9	2.4	2.6
65–69	3	6	9	1.3	1.0	1.1
70–74	2	6	8	0.8	1.0	0.9
75–79	1	1	2	0.4	0.2	0.2
Total	238	616	854	100.0	100.0	100.0

TABLE 63—Non-Jewish white first admissions with manic-depressive psychoses to all hospitals for mental disease in New York State, 1939-1941, classified according to age.

Age (years)	Number			Per cent		
	Males	Females	Total	Males	Females	Total
10–14	2	2	4	0.2	0.1	0.2
15–19	29	58	87	3.4	3.4	3.4
20–24	89	179	268	10.5	10.6	10.6
25–29	82	209	291	9.6	12.4	11.5
30–34	82	290	372	9.6	17.3	14.7
35–39	98	286	384	11.5	17.0	15.2
40–44	105	191	296	12.4	11.4	11.7
45–49	135	142	277	15.9	8.4	10.9
50–54	99	133	232	11.7	7.9	9.2
55–59	67	80	147	7.9	4.8	5.8
60–64	44	58	102	5.2	3.4	4.0
65–69	12	38	50	1.4	2.3	2.0
70–74	4	14	18	0.4	0.8	0.7
75–79	1	—	1	0.1	—	*
80–84	1	1	2	0.1	0.1	0.1
Total	850	1681	2531	100.0	100.0	100.0

*Less than 0.05.

TABLE 64—Jewish and non-Jewish white first admissions with manic-depressive psychoses to all hospitals for mental disease in New York State, 1939-1941, classified according to age and rate per 100,000 population.

Age (years)	Jews					Non-Jews				
	Males	Females	Total		Average annual rate per 100,000	Males	Females	Total		Average annual rate per 100,000
			No.	Per cent				No.	Per cent	
10–14........	—	1	1	0.1	0.2	2	2	4	0.2	0.2
15–19........	17	27	44	5.2	8.5	29	58	87	3.4	3.2
20–24........	16	67	83	9.7	13.8	89	179	268	10.6	10.0
25–34........	64	170	234	27.4	18.9	164	499	663	26.2	12.4
35–44........	70	191	261	30.6	22.9	203	477	680	26.9	13.4
45–54........	49	111	160	18.7	17.3	234	275	509	20.1	11.7
55–64........	16	36	52	6.1	9.4	111	138	249	9.8	8.6
65 and over...	6	13	19	2.2	5.7	18	53	71	2.8	3.0
Total....	238	616	854	100.0	12.9	850	1681	2531	100.0	7.9

TABLE 65—Jewish and non-Jewish white first admissions with manic-depressive psychoses, from New York City, to all hospitals for mental disease in New York State, 1939-1941, classified according to age and rate per 100,000 population.

Age (years)	Jews					Non-Jews				
	Males	Females	Total		Average annual rate per 100,000	Males	Females	Total		Average annual rate per 100,000
			No.	Per cent				No.	Per cent	
10–14........	—	1	1	0.1	0.2	—	—	—	—	—
15–19........	16	21	37	4.9	7.8	11	27	38	3.2	3.1
20–24........	15	59	74	9.9	13.3	43	86	129	10.8	10.2
25–34........	45	150	195	26.0	17.1	73	252	325	27.2	12.0
35–44........	64	180	244	32.6	23.2	112	246	358	30.0	14.1
45–54........	42	94	136	18.2	15.9	108	119	227	19.0	11.2
55–64........	14	32	46	6.1	9.1	42	57	99	8.3	7.8
65 and over...	3	13	16	2.1	5.2	3	16	19	1.6	2.1
Total....	199	550	749	100.0	12.3	392	803	1195	100.0	8.1

needed for determining the rates according to nativity are not available. It has been shown, however, that there is no significant difference between total native and foreign-born whites with respect to manic-depressive psychoses.[2]

TABLE 66—Foreign-born Jewish first admissions with manic-depressive psychoses to all hospitals for mental disease in New York State, 1939–1941, classified according to age and nativity.

Age (years)	Russia			Poland			Austria			Germany			Hungary			Roumania		
	M	F	T	M	F	T	M	F	T	M	F	T	M	F	T	M	F	T
15–19	—	—	—	—	1	1	—	—	—	—	—	—	—	1	1	—	—	—
20–24	—	—	—	—	1	1	—	—	—	—	—	—	—	—	—	—	1	1
25–29	—	5	5	3	3	6	—	1	1	—	9	9	—	1	1	—	—	—
30–34	3	3	6	1	4	5	3	6	9	—	4	4	—	6	6	—	3	3
35–39	2	26	28	1	10	11	—	1	1	2	4	6	—	—	—	—	2	2
40–44	14	25	39	5	8	13	1	9	10	—	4	4	1	1	2	—	1	1
45–49	9	20	29	—	8	8	1	16	17	2	3	5	1	1	2	1	—	1
50–54	12	14	26	2	5	7	3	3	6	1	—	1	—	—	—	—	1	1
55–59	5	4	9	1	4	5	2	—	2	—	3	3	—	—	—	—	—	—
60–64	—	3	3	—	—	—	4	6	10	1	—	1	—	—	—	1	—	1
65–69	3	3	6	—	—	—	—	—	—	—	—	—	—	—	—	—	—	—
70–74	1	—	1	—	—	—	1	—	1	—	—	—	—	—	—	—	—	—
75–79	—	—	—	—	—	—	—	1	1	—	—	—	—	—	—	—	—	—
Total	49	103	152	13	44	57	15	43	58	6	27	33	2	10	12	2	8	10

TABLE 67—Native Jewish first admissions with manic-depressive psychoses to all hospitals for mental disease in New York State, 1939–1941, classified according to age and nativity of parents.

Age (years)	Russia			Poland			Austria			Germany			Hungary			Roumania		
	M	F	T	M	F	T	M	F	T	M	F	T	M	F	T	M	F	T
15–19	8	10	18	1	—	1	1	3	4	—	—	—	—	3	3	2	3	5
20–24	8	30	38	3	8	11	1	10	11	—	—	—	1	—	1	1	—	1
25–29	16	23	39	1	9	10	—	12	12	—	3	3	1	5	6	—	7	7
30–34	10	28	38	2	7	9	6	7	13	—	1	1	—	—	—	4	9	13
35–39	11	40	51	—	10	10	3	11	14	—	3	3	—	3	3	1	—	1
40–44	9	11	20	—	1	1	4	5	9	3	3	6	—	4	4	—	1	1
45–49	4	15	19	—	—	—	4	7	11	—	4	4	—	1	1	—	1	1
50–54	—	2	2	—	3	3	—	—	—	—	1	1	1	2	3	—	—	—
55–59	—	—	—	—	—	—	—	4	4	—	—	—	—	—	—	—	—	—
60–64	—	1	1	—	—	—	—	—	—	—	3	3	—	1	1	—	—	—
65–69	—	—	—	—	—	—	—	—	—	—	—	—	—	—	—	—	—	—
70–74	—	1	1	—	—	—	—	—	—	—	1	1	—	—	—	—	—	—
Total	66	161	227	7	38	45	19	59	78	3	19	22	3	19	22	8	21	29

Of the 359 foreign-born Jewish first admissions, 152, or 42.1 per cent, were born in Russia. The other groups were all of small numerical order. Those born in Poland, Austria and Germany numbered 57, 58, and 33, respectively.

To the foreign-born, we may add the natives of foreign parentage. The largest group, 227, were of Russian parentage. Thus, 379, or 45.5 per cent of the total Jewish first admissions with manic-depressive psychoses were of Russian origin. No other group was of comparable size. The rates cannot be computed, however, because of the lack of essential data.

Environment

All but 2 of the 854 Jewish first admissions with manic-depressive psychoses were from urban areas. The great majority were from New York City. It is interesting, however, that 12.1 per cent were from urban areas outside New York City, whereas the corresponding percentage for all Jewish first admissions was only 7.

The urban-rural distribution was significantly different for non-Jews. Ninety per cent were from urban, and 10 per cent from rural areas. However, the urban first admissions were divided about equally between New York City and the remaining urban areas of New York State.

TABLE 68—Jewish and non-Jewish white first admissions with manic-depressive psychoses to all hospitals for mental disease in New York State, 1939-1941, classified according to environment and nativity.

Environment	Jews		Non-Jews		Native Jews		Native non-Jews		Foreign-born Jews		Foreign-born non-Jews	
	No.	Per cent	No.	Per cent	No.	Per cent	No.	Per cent	No.	Per cent	No.	Per cent
Urban	852	99.8	2276	89.9	493	99.6	1724	88.0	359	100.0	552	96.7
New York City	749	87.7	1195	47.2	424	85.7	834	42.6	326	90.8	360	63.1
Other	103	12.1	1081	42.7	69	13.9	890	45.4	33	9.2	192	33.6
Rural	2	0.2	255	10.1	2	0.4	236	12.0	—	—	19	3.3
Farm	—	—	64	2.5	—	—	60	3.1	—	—	4	0.7
Non-farm	2	0.2	191	7.5	2	0.4	176	9.0	—	—	15.	2.6
Total	854	100.0	2531	100.0	495	100.0	1960	100.0	359	100.0	571	100.0

Use of Alcohol

Of the 854 Jewish first admissions with manic-depressive psychoses, 10, or 1.2 per cent, were intemperate users of alcohol, compared with 8.8 per cent of non-Jews. The percentages were less than the corresponding percentages for all Jewish and non-Jewish first admissions, excluding those with alcoholic psychoses.

Of the foreign-born Jews, 0.3 per cent were intemperate, compared with 1.8 per cent of native Jewish first admissions. Among non-Jewish first admissions, native and foreign-born had the same percentage of intemperates. There is a suggestion that intemperance may have increased among native-born Jews.

TABLE 69—Jewish and non-Jewish white first admissions with manic-depressive psychoses to all hospitals for mental disease in New York State, 1939-1941, classified according to use of alcohol and nativity.

Use of alcohol	Jews		Non-Jews		Native Jews		Native non-Jews		Foreign-born Jews		Foreign-born non-Jews	
	No.	Per cent	No.	Per cent	No.	Per cent	No.	Per cent	No.	Per cent	No.	Per cent
Abstinent	600	70.3	1236	48.8	339	68.4	949	48.4	264	73.5	284	49.7
Moderate	189	22.1	980	38.7	117	23.6	766	39.1	69	19.2	217	38.0
Intemperate	10	1.2	223	8.8	9	1.8	173	8.8	1	0.3	50	8.8
Unascertained	55	6.4	92	3.6	30	6.1	72	3.7	25	7.0	20	3.5
Total	854	100.0	2531	100.0	495	100.0	1960	100.0	359	100.0	571	100.0

Summary

Jews have a significantly higher rate of first admissions with manic-depressive psychoses than non-Jews.

REFERENCES

1. *See,* Roberts, B. H. and J. K. Myers. "Religion, National Origin, Immigration and Mental Illness." American Journal of Psychiatry. 110:759. April, 1954.

2. Malzberg, Benjamin. "Mental Disease Among Native and Foreign-born White Populations of New York State, 1939-1941. Mental Hygiene. Vol. 39. No. 4, October, 1955.

PART VIII

Dementia Praecox

THE largest group of first admissions is dementia praecox. Of the 6987 Jewish first admissions, 2152, or 30.8 per cent, were in this category. Of the non-Jewish first admissions, 22.4 per cent were so diagnosed. The total white first admissions with dementia praecox was 10,113, of whom 21.2 per cent were Jews, and 78.7 per cent, non-Jews. Since Jews included 16.4 per cent of all white first admissions, they were over-represented among those with dementia praecox, and non-Jews were correspondingly underrepresented. Whether this implies a higher rate of first admissions with dementia praecox among Jews will be discussed subsequently.

Of the Jewish first admissions, 16.9 per cent were admitted to licensed hospitals. This is twice the corresponding percentage for non-Jews. It is less than the corresponding percentage for all Jewish first admissions, and much below that for manic-depressive psychoses. It is probably associated with class (economic) differences. Thus, about 30 per cent of Jewish first admissions with manic-depressive psychoses were classified as in comfortable economic circumstances, compared with 11 per cent of those with dementia praecox. A similar difference occurred among non-Jews, of whom 23 per cent of manic-depressives were in comfortable circumstances, compared with only 9.6 per cent of those with dementia praecox.

TABLE 70—Jewish and non-Jewish white first admissions with dementia praecox to all hospitals for mental disease in New York State, 1939-1941, classified according to type of hospital and nativity.

	Jews		Non-Jews		Native Jews		Native non-Jews		Foreign-born Jews		Foreign-born non-Jews	
	No.	Per cent	No.	Per cent	No.	Per cent	No.	Per cent	No.	Per cent	No.	Per cent
Civil State hospitals..	1781	82.8	7179	90.2	1196	82.3	5343	88.7	585	83.7	1836	94.8
Hospitals for criminal insane............	8	0.4	92	1.2	5	0.3	66	1.1	3	0.4	26	1.3
Licensed hospitals....	363	16.9	690	8.7	252	17.3	615	10.2	111	15.9	75	3.9
Total..........	2152	100.0	7961	100.0	1453	100.0	6024	100.0	699	100.0	1937	100.0

TABLE 71—Jewish first admissions with dementia praecox to all hospitals for mental disease in New York State, 1939-1941, classified according to age.

Age (years)	Number			Per cent		
	Males	Females	Total	Males	Females	Total
10–14	17	5	22	1.7	0.4	1.0
15–19	186	138	324	18.4	12.1	15.1
20–24	245	195	440	24.2	17.1	20.4
25–29	196	222	418	19.4	19.4	19.4
30–34	151	174	325	14.9	15.3	15.1
35–39	106	175	281	10.4	15.4	13.1
40–44	57	103	160	5.6	9.0	7.4
45–49	27	67	94	2.7	5.9	4.4
50–54	12	26	38	1.2	2.3	1.8
55–59	8	21	29	0.8	1.8	1.3
60–64	3	11	14	0.3	1.0	0.7
65–69	4	—	4	0.4	—	0.2
70–74	—	3	3	—	0.3	0.1
Total	1012	1140	2152	100.0	100.0	100.0

TABLE 72—Non-Jewish white first admissions with dementia praecox to all hospitals for mental disease in New York State, 1939-1941, classified according to age.

Age (years)	Number			Per cent		
	Males	Females	Total	Males	Females	Total
10–14	7	21	28	0.2	0.5	0.4
15–19	350	293	643	8.5	7.6	8.1
20–24	777	553	1330	18.9	14.4	16.7
25–29	778	676	1454	18.9	17.6	18.3
30–34	671	608	1279	16.3	15.8	16.1
35–39	547	590	1137	13.3	15.3	14.3
40–44	402	408	810	9.8	10.6	10.2
45–49	289	307	596	7.0	8.0	7.4
50–54	162	194	356	3.9	5.0	4.4
55–59	89	110	199	2.2	2.9	2.5
60–64	29	46	75	0.7	1.2	0.9
65–69	9	27	36	0.2	0.7	0.4
70–74	—	6	6	—	0.2	0.1
75–79	4	5	9	0.1	0.1	0.1
80–84	—	1	1	—	*	*
85–89	—	2	2	—	0.1	*
Total	4114	3847	7961	100.0	100.0	100.0

*Less than 0.05.

Age

Of the 2152 Jewish first admissions with dementia praecox, more than half were under 30 years of age. The average age was 30.1 years. Males were significantly younger than females, the average ages being 28.2 and 31.8 years, respectively.

Non-Jewish first admissions were significantly older than Jews. The average was 33.6 years. Males and females had average ages of 32.7 and 34.4 years, respectively.

Rate

The rate of first admissions rose among Jews from 4.6 per 100,000 among those aged 10 to 14 to a maximum of 73.0 at 20 to 24 years. The rate declined steadily at older ages. The trend was similar among non-Jews, with a maximum at ages 25 to 34. Through ages 25 to 34, the rates for Jews were in marked excess. Beyond age 45, Jews had lower rates. The average rate for Jews however, was 32.5, compared with 24.9 for non-Jews. When standardized on a similar basis as for all first admissions, the rates became 38.6 for Jews and 31.6 for non-Jews.

Dementia praecox is most frequent among urban populations.[1] Such rates are highest for New York City. Since the great majority of Jews are in New York City, a more equitable comparison may be made by considering first admissions from that city. This is a closer approach to a constant environment. The data are shown in Table 74.

Jews had higher rates than non-Jews at ages under 25. But the excess was in a smaller ratio than for the whole State. Beyond age 25, Jews had lower rates than non-Jews. The average rates were 32.8 and 32.2 for Jews and non-Jews, respectively. Obviously, this is not a significant difference.

We may standardize the rates on the basis of the age distribution of the white population of New York State on April 1, 1940, in appropriate intervals beginning at age 15. The standardized rates were 39.0 and 38.8, respectively. If we consider that the Jewish general population must have been underestimated, it follows that the rate for Jews should be decreased. This would also result in an increase of the rate for non-Jews. Without pushing the argument, it must be concluded that, the data for New York City imply that there is no difference between Jews and non-Jews in rates of first admissions with dementia praecox.

Nativity

Of the 2152 Jewish first admissions with dementia praecox, 1453, or 67.5 per cent were native, and 699, or 32.5 per cent, were foreign-born. A similar excess of native-born is seen among non-Jews. In both cases, this was due to the association of dementia praecox with younger age groups. Whether the corresponding rates of first admissions, corrected for age, vary in the same order, we do not know, because the necessary data are lacking. It is known however, that for the white population as a whole, natives had a lower rate of first admissions with dementia praecox than foreign-born.[2]

TABLE 73—Jewish and non-Jewish white first admissions with dementia praecox to all hospitals for mental disease in New York State, 1939-1941, classified according to age and rate per 100,000 population.

Age (years)	Jews					Non-Jews				
	Males	Females	Total		Average annual rate per 100,000	Males	Females	Total		Average annual rate per 100,000
			No.	Per cent				No.	Per cent	
10–14........	17	5	22	1.0	4.6	7	21	28	0.4	1.1
15–19........	186	138	324	15.1	62.8	350	293	643	8.1	23.7
20–24........	245	195	440	20.4	73.0	777	553	1330	16.7	49.7
25–34........	347	396	743	34.5	60.0	1449	1284	2733	34.3	51.1
35–44........	163	278	441	20.5	38.7	949	998	1947	24.4	38.6
45–54........	39	93	132	6.1	14.2	451	501	952	12.0	22.0
55–64........	11	32	43	2.0	7.8	118	156	274	3.4	9.5
65 and over...	4	3	7	0.3	2.1	13	41	54	0.7	2.3
Total....	1012	1140	2152	100.0	32.5	4114	3847	7961	100.0	24.9

TABLE 74—Jewish and non-Jewish white first admissions with dementia praecox, from New Tork City, to all hospitals for mental disease in New York State, 1939-1941, classified according to age and rate per 100,000 population.

Age (years)	Jews					Non-Jews				
	Males	Females	Total		Average annual rate per 100,000	Males	Females	Total		Average annual rate per 100,000
			No.	Per cent				No.	Per cent	
10–14........	16	5	21	1.0	4.8	5	12	17	0.4	1.5
15–19........	173	132	305	15.2	64.1	215	168	383	8.0	30.9
20–24........	220	178	398	19.9	71.6	462	339	801	16.8	63.3
25–34........	323	377	700	35.0	61.3	891	770	1661	34.8	61.4
35–44........	152	266	418	20.9	39.8	594	597	1191	24.9	46.8
45–54........	32	87	119	5.9	13.9	275	284	559	11.7	27.5
55–64........	9	28	37	1.9	7.3	55	91	146	3.1	11.6
65 and over..	4	—	4	0.2	1.3	4	15	19	0.4	2.1
Total....	929	1073	2002	100.0	32.8	2501	2276	4777	100.0	32.2

The largest group of foreign-born Jewish first admissions with dementia praecox were from Russia. They numbered 289, or 41.3 per cent of the total foreign-born. Those born in Poland were second with a total of 174. Other nationalities were represented as follows: Austria, 78, Germany, 36, Hungary, 35, Roumania, 24.

TABLE 75—Foreign-born Jewish first admissions with dementia praecox to all hospitals for mental disease in New York State, 1939–1941, classified according to age and nativity.

Age (years)	Russia			Poland			Austria			Germany			Hungary			Roumania		
	M	F	T	M	F	T	M	F	T	M	F	T	M	F	T	M	F	T
15–19	1	3	4	4	2	6	3	1	4	3	1	4	—	—	—	—	—	—
20–24	8	6	14	6	4	10	4	4	8	2	3	5	—	2	2	—	—	—
25–29	13	19	32	20	15	35	5	4	9	2	5	7	2	1	3	3	—	3
30–34	20	29	49	22	16	38	3	10	13	5	2	7	—	3	3	1	1	2
35–39	20	50	70	18	16	34	5	7	12	—	6	6	3	11	14	2	2	4
40–44	17	37	54	6	18	24	5	4	9	1	2	3	—	1	1	—	7	7
45–49	9	20	29	3	13	16	4	8	12	—	3	3	1	2	3	—	3	3
50–54	5	16	21	3	2	5	3	—	3	—	1	1	1	2	3	—	2	2
55–59	5	9	14	—	1	1	—	2	2	—	—	—	1	3	4	—	2	2
60–64	—	1	1	1	1	2	1	5	6	—	—	—	—	2	2	—	1	1
65–69	1	—	1	—	—	—	—	—	—	—	—	—	—	—	—	—	—	—
70–74	—	—	—	—	3	3	—	—	—	—	—	—	—	—	—	—	—	—
Total	99	190	289	83	91	174	33	45	78	13	23	36	8	27	35	6	18	24

TABLE 76—Native Jewish first admissions with dementia praecox to all hospitals for mental disease in New York State, 1939–1941, classified according to age and nativity of parents.

Age (years)	Russia			Poland			Austria			Germany			Hungary			Roumania		
	M	F	T	M	F	T	M	F	T	M	F	T	M	F	T	M	F	T
10–14	9	2	11	2	1	3	2	1	3	—	—	—	—	—	—	—	—	—
15–19	84	70	154	23	15	38	17	18	35	—	1	1	4	5	9	10	3	13
20–24	116	109	225	23	20	43	33	17	50	1	2	3	4	6	10	10	12	22
25–29	82	93	175	14	16	30	24	21	45	3	1	4	4	8	12	6	10	16
30–34	46	58	104	12	9	21	11	18	29	7	3	10	5	3	8	5	2	7
35–39	23	35	58	8	9	17	11	10	21	9	1	10	2	3	5	—	4	4
40–44	9	13	22	2	4	6	7	7	14	1	—	1	—	2	2	1	1	2
45–49	2	6	8	—	—	—	5	1	6	1	—	1	—	1	1	—	2	2
50–54	—	1	1	—	—	—	1	1	2	—	—	—	—	—	—	—	—	—
55–59	—	1	1	—	—	—	—	—	—	—	1	1	—	—	—	—	—	—
60–64	—	—	—	—	—	—	—	1	1	—	—	—	—	—	—	—	—	—
65–69	—	—	—	—	—	—	—	—	—	3	—	3	—	—	—	—	—	—
Total	371	388	759	84	74	158	111	95	206	25	9	34	19	28	47	32	34	66

Together with the foreign-born, we may consider native Jews of foreign parentage. The outstanding group was that with Russian parentage, who numbered 759. Thus, those either born in Russia, or of Russian parentage included 1048, or 48.7 per cent of total Jewish first admissions with dementia praecox. Other groups with foreign parentage are shown in Table 76. Because of the absence of data for the corresponding general populations, it is not possible to compute rates of first admissions according to nativity and parentage.

Environment

Of the 2152 Jewish first admissions with dementia praecox, 2140, or 99.4 per cent, were from an urban environment. New York City was the primary locus, with 93 per cent of the total. This differs significantly from non-Jews. Of the latter, 60 per cent were from New York City, and 32.2 per cent were from the remaining urban areas of New York State.

TABLE 77—Jewish and non-Jewish white first admissions with dementia praecox to all hospitals for mental disease in New York State, 1939-1941, classified according to environment and nativity.

Environment	Jews		Non-Jews		Native Jews		Native non-Jews		Foreign-born Jews		Foreign-born non-Jews	
	No.	Per cent	No.	Per cent	No.	Per cent	No.	Per cent	No.	Per cent	No.	Per cent
Urban	2140	99.4	7342	92.2	1444	99.4	5477	90.9	697	99.7	1864	96.2
New York City	2002	93.0	4777	60.0	1346	92.6	3361	55.8	657	94.0	1415	73.1
Other	138	6.4	2565	32.2	98	6.7	2116	35.1	40	5.7	449	23.2
Rural	12	0.6	619	7.8	9	0.6	547	9.1	2	0.3	73	3.8
Farm	3	0.1	175	2.2	1	0.1	162	2.7	1	0.1	14	0.7
Non-farm	9	0.4	444	5.6	8	0.5	385	6.4	1	0.1	59	3.0
Total	2152	100.0	7961	100.0	1453	100.0	6024	100.0	699	100.0	1937	100.0

TABLE 78—Jewish and non-Jewish white first admissions with dementia praecox to all hospitals for mental disease in New York State, 1939-1941, classified according to use of alcohol and nativity.

Use of alcohol	Jews		Non-Jews		Native Jews		Native non-Jews		Foreign-born Jews		Foreign-born non-Jews	
	No.	Per cent	No.	Per cent	No.	Per cent	No.	Per cent	No.	Per cent	No.	Per cent
Abstinent	1693	78.7	4206	52.8	1136	78.2	3272	54.3	557	79.7	934	48.2
Moderate	356	16.5	2800	35.2	249	17.1	2063	34.2	107	15.3	737	38.0
Intemperate	19	0.9	694	8.7	12	0.8	481	8.0	7	1.0	213	11.0
Unascertained	84	3.9	261	3.3	56	3.9	208	3.5	28	4.0	53	2.7
Total	2152	100.0	7961	100.0	1453	100.0	6024	100.0	699	100.0	1937	100.0

Use of alcohol

Only 0.9 per cent of the Jewish first admissions with dementia praecox used alcohol intemperately, compared with 8.7 per cent of non-Jews. Both are low, compared with corresponding percentages for all first admissions excluding alcoholic psychoses. This is due, in large part, to the higher percentage of younger admissions with dementia praecox. Those in middle life have higher percentages of intemperate drinkers.

Summary

When age and degree of urbanization are considered, there is no significant difference between Jews and non-Jews with respect to the relative frequency of dementia praecox.

REFERENCES

1. Malzberg, Benjamin. Social and Biological Aspects of Mental Disease. State Hospitals Press. Utica, New York. 1940, Chapter II.

2. Malzberg, Benjamin. Mental Disease Among Native and Foreign-born White Populations of New York State, 1939-1941. Mental Hygiene. Vol. 39, No. 4. October, 1955.

PART IX

Psychoneuroses

THOUGH many different reasons have been offered to explain the fact, there is complete agreement that Jews have a greater frequency of psychoneuroses than non-Jews. This is readily confirmed by reference to Table 2. Thus, of the 6987 Jewish first admissions to all hospitals for mental disease in New York State in 1939-1941, 550, or 7.9 per cent, were classified as psychoneuroses, compared with 4.9 per cent of non-Jews. Jews constituted 16.4 per cent of the total white admissions, but 23.9 per cent of the total with psychoneuroses. Non-Jews, on the contrary, were underrepresented, including only 76.1 per cent of the total with psychoneuroses, but 83.6 per cent of all white first admissions.

Of the Jewish first admissions with psychoneuroses, 61.1 per cent were admitted to licensed hospitals, compared with 35.9 per cent of non-Jews. The higher percentage for Jews was due primarily to the greater esteem in which Jews hold the private practice of psychiatry. But both Jewish and non-Jewish first admissions with psychoneuroses use private facilities more than any other group of first admissions. This is due in part to their economic status, 26 per cent of the Jews and 29.6 per cent of the non-Jews being classified as in comfortable economic circumstances compared with 14.7 per cent of all Jewish first admissions, and 13 per cent of all non-Jewish first admissions.

TABLE 79—Jewish and non-Jewish white first admissions with psychoneuroses to all hospitals for mental disease in New York State, 1939-1941, classified according to type of hospital and nativity.

	Jews		Non-Jews		Native Jews		Native non-Jews		Foreign-born Jews		Foreign-born non-Jews	
	No.	Per cent	No.	Per cent	No.	Per cent	No.	Per cent	No.	Per cent	No.	Per cent
Civil State hospitals	210	38.2	1107	63.3	133	41.7	897	63.3	77	33.3	210	63.4
Hospitals for criminal insane	4	0.7	14	0.8	3	0.9	7	0.5	1	0.4	7	2.1
Licensed hospitals	336	61.1	627	35.9	183	57.4	513	36.2	153	66.2	114	34.4
Total	550	100.0	1748	100.0	319	100.0	1417	100.0	231	100.0	331	100.0

TABLE 80—Jewish first admissions with psychoneuroses to all hospitals for mental disease in New York State, 1939-1941, classified according to age.

Age (years)	Number			Per cent		
	Males	Females	Total	Males	Females	Total
5–9	2	—	2	0.8	—	0.4
10–14	2	2	4	0.8	0.7	0.7
15–19	12	14	26	4.8	4.7	4.7
20–24	25	29	54	10.0	9.7	9.8
25–29	30	49	79	12.0	16.3	14.4
30–34	35	43	78	14.0	14.3	14.2
35–39	29	36	65	11.6	12.0	11.8
40–44	50	46	96	20.0	15.3	17.4
45–49	24	28	52	9.6	9.3	9.4
50–54	18	35	53	7.2	11.7	9.6
55–59	12	10	22	4.8	3.3	4.0
60–64	6	1	7	2.4	0.3	1.3
65–69	5	5	10	2.0	1.7	1.8
70–74	—	2	2	—	0.7	0.4
Total	250	300	550	100.0	100.0	100.0

TABLE 81—Non-Jewish white first admissions with psychoneuroses to all hospitals for mental disease in New York State, 1939-1941, classified according to age.

Age (years)	Number			Per cent		
	Males	Females	Total	Males	Females	Total
5–9	—	1	1	—	0.1	0.1
10–14	5	6	11	0.7	0.6	0.6
15–19	17	32	49	2.2	3.2	2.8
20–24	51	71	122	6.7	7.2	7.0
25–29	63	156	219	8.3	15.7	12.5
30–34	98	142	240	12.9	14.3	13.7
35–39	103	139	242	13.6	14.0	13.8
40–44	105	118	223	13.9	11.9	12.8
45–49	107	77	184	14.1	7.8	10.5
50–54	87	89	176	11.5	9.0	10.1
55–59	67	66	133	8.9	6.7	7.6
60–64	38	52	90	5.0	5.2	5.1
65–69	15	29	44	2.0	2.9	2.5
70–74	—	11	11	—	1.1	0.6
75–79	1	—	1	0.1	—	0.1
80–84	—	2	2	—	0.2	0.1
Total	757	991	1748	100.0	100.0	100.0

Age

Jewish first admissions with psychoneuroses had an average age of 37.7 years. Males and females did not differ significantly, the average ages being 37.9 and 37.5 years, respectively. The admissions were concentrated largely between 25 and 44 years.

Non-Jewish first admissions with psychoneuroses were older than Jews. They had an average age of 40.8 years, compared with 37.7 for Jews. Non-Jewish males, with an average age of 41.9 years were older than non-Jewish females, who had an average age of 40 years. Both were in significant excess over the corresponding ages for Jews.

Rate

Average annual rates of first admissions rose among Jews from 0.4 per 100,000 at ages 5 to 9 to 14.1 at ages 45 to 54. With one exception, Jews had higher rates than non-Jews at each age level (See Table 82). The average annual rate was 8.3 for Jews and 5.4 for non-Jews. The former was in excess by 54 per cent. If the rates are standardized with respect to age, using the same standard as for dementia praecox, the rates become 10.0 for Jews and 6.9 for non-Jews, an excess of 45 per cent. We do not have data with respect to non-Jewish first admissions from New York City, and we cannot, therefore, compare Jews and non-Jews without some attention to gross environmental differences. There is no reason for believing that differential rates

TABLE 82—Jewish and non-Jewish white first admissions with psychoneuroses to all hospitals for mental disease in New York State, 1939-1941, classified according to age and rate per 100,000 population.

Age (years)	Jews					Non-Jews				
	Males	Fe-males	Total		Average annual rate per 100,000	Males	Fe-males	Total		Average annual rate per 100,000
			No.	Per cent				No.	Per cent	
5–9	2	—	2	0.8	0.4	—	1	1	0.1	*
10–14	2	2	4	0.8	0.8	5	6	11	0.6	0.4
15–19	12	14	26	4.8	5.0	17	32	49	2.8	1.8
20–24	25	29	54	10.0	9.0	51	71	122	7.0	4.6
25–34	65	92	157	26.0	12.7	161	298	459	26.3	8.6
35–44	79	82	161	31.6	14.1	208	257	465	26.6	9.2
45–54	42	63	105	16.8	11.3	194	166	360	20.6	8.3
55–64	18	11	29	7.2	5.3	105	118	223	12.8	7.7
65 and over	5	7	12	2.0	3.6	16	42	58	3.3	2.4
Total	250	300	550	100.0	8.3	757	991	1748	100.0	5.4

*Less than 0.05.

of first admissions with such disorders would differ if such data were available. As with the manic-depressive psychoses, it is improbable that a correction of the estimate of the Jewish general population would alter the fact of a Jewish excess of such disorders.

Nativity

Of 550 Jewish first admissions with psychoneuroses, 319, or 58 per cent, were native, and 231, or 42 per cent, were foreign-born. The excess of the native-born is due in part to the fact that these disorders are relatively more

TABLE 83—Foreign-born first admissions with psychoneuroses to all hospitals for mental disease in New York State, 1939–1941, classified according to age and nativity.

Age (years)	Russia			Poland			Austria			Germany			Hungary			Roumania		
	M	F	T	M	F	T	M	F	T	M	F	T	M	F	T	M	F	T
20–24	—	1	1	4	1	5	1	—	1	—	3	3	—	—	—	—	—	—
25–29	1	2	3	4	1	5	—	5	5	—	—	—	—	—	—	—	—	—
30–34	2	1	3	1	4	5	1	—	1	—	1	1	1	—	1	—	—	—
35–39	4	16	20	—	—	—	—	—	—	—	—	—	—	—	—	—	3	3
40–44	6	13	19	4	4	8	—	2	2	3	—	3	1	6	7	—	3	3
45–49	9	7	16	3	1	4	1	6	7	—	3	3	—	—	—	—	—	—
50–54	8	18	26	4	2	6	4	7	11	—	3	3	—	—	—	—	—	—
55–59	5	2	7	—	4	4	3	3	6	—	—	—	1	—	1	—	3	3
60–64	4	1	5	—	—	—	—	—	—	—	1	1	1	—	1	—	—	—
65–69	2	—	2	—	—	—	—	—	—	3	1	4	—	—	—	—	—	—
70–74	—	—	—	—	—	—	—	—	—	—	—	—	—	1	1	—	—	—
Total	41	61	102	20	17	37	10	23	33	6	12	18	4	7	11	—	9	9

TABLE 84—Native Jewish first admissions with psychoneuroses to all hospitals for mental disease in New York State, 1939–1941, classified according to age and nativity of parents.

Age (years)	Russia			Poland			Austria			Germany			Hungary			Roumania		
	M	F	T	M	F	T	M	F	T	M	F	T	M	F	T	M	F	T
10–14	—	1	1	1	—	1	—	—	—	—	—	—	—	—	—	—	—	—
15–19	5	12	17	—	1	1	1	—	1	—	—	—	1	—	1	—	—	—
20–24	9	7	16	1	1	2	1	6	7	—	—	—	—	—	—	—	—	—
25–29	13	23	36	1	4	5	4	7	11	—	6	6	2	—	2	2	—	2
30–34	14	21	35	4	6	10	4	7	11	1	—	1	—	—	—	1	—	1
35–39	7	6	13	1	—	1	5	6	11	—	—	—	1	1	2	3	3	6
40–44	16	10	26	4	3	7	6	3	9	4	3	7	3	1	4	—	—	—
45–49	2	6	8	1	—	1	1	1	2	—	—	—	3	—	3	—	—	—
50–54	1	—	1	—	—	—	1	—	1	—	2	2	—	—	—	—	—	—
55–59	3	—	3	—	—	—	—	1	1	—	—	—	—	—	—	—	—	—
60–64	1	—	1	—	—	—	—	—	—	—	—	—	—	—	—	—	—	—
65–69	—	—	—	—	—	—	—	—	—	—	—	—	—	—	—	—	—	—
70–74	—	1	1	—	—	—	—	—	—	—	—	—	—	—	—	—	—	—
Total	71	87	158	13	15	28	23	31	54	5	11	16	10	2	12	6	3	9

prevalent at younger ages, from which come the larger proportion of such admissions. However, foreign-born Jews constitute 35 per cent of total Jews, and it therefore appears they contributed more than their quota to the total of Jewish first admissions with psychoneuroses. We cannot complete the analysis of the differences, because all the essential data are not available.

Of the 231 foreign-born Jews, 102, or 44.2 per cent, were born in Russia. No other foreign-born group was of equal numerical importance. If to the foreign-born, we add natives of foreign parentage, we have an additional group of 158 for Russia. Thus the total who were either born in Russia or of Russian parentage was 260 out of a total of 550 Jewish first admissions, or 47.3 per cent. Corresponding percentages for Poland and Austria were only 10 and 16, respectively. Unfortunately, rates of first admissions per 100,000 corresponding population cannot be computed, because of lack of necessary population statistics.

TABLE 85—Jewish and non-Jewish white first admissions with psychoneuroses to all hospitals for mental disease in New York State, 1939-1941, classified according to environment and nativity.

Environment	Jews		Non-Jews		Native Jews		Native non-Jews		Foreign-born Jews		Foreign-born non-Jews	
	No.	Per cent	No.	Per cent	No.	Per cent	No.	Per cent	No.	Per cent	No.	Per cent
Urban	548	99.6	1542	88.2	317	99.4	1236	87.2	231	100.0	306	92.4
New York City	487	88.5	733	41.9	279	87.5	538	38.0	212	91.8	191	57.7
Other	61	11.1	809	46.3	38	11.9	698	49.3	19	8.2	115	34.7
Rural	2	0.4	206	11.8	2	0.6	181	12.8	—	—	25	7.6
Farm	—	—	50	2.9	—	—	41	2.9	—	—	9	2.7
Non-farm	2	0.4	156	8.9	2	0.6	149	9.9	—	—	16	4.8
Total	550	100.0	1748	100.0	319	100.0	1417	100.0	231	100.0	331	100.0

Environment

Of the 550 Jewish first admissions with psychoneuroses, 548, or 99.6 per cent, were from urban environments. Of the total, 88.5 per cent were from New York City, and 11.1 per cent were from other urban areas. The non-Jews were also predominantly urban, but to a lesser degree than Jews. The significant difference lies in the fact that only 41.9 per cent were from New York City and 46.3 per cent were from the remainder of the urban areas of New York State.

Use of alcohol

As with all other groups of first admissions the percentage of intemperance was much less for Jewish first admissions. The percentages were 2.0 and 9.9 for Jews and non-Jews, respectively. The percentage for Jews did not differ significantly from the average for all Jewish first admissions, but that for non-Jews was less than their corresponding average.

TABLE 86—Jewish and non-Jewish white first admissions with psychoneuroses to all hospitals for mental disease in New York State, 1939-1941, classified according to use of alcohol and nativity.

Use of alcohol	Jews		Non-Jews		Native Jews		Native non-Jews		Foreign-born Jews		Foreign-born non-Jews	
	No.	Per cent	No.	Per cent	No.	Per cent	No.	Per cent	No.	Per cent	No.	Per cent
Abstinent	318	57.8	843	48.2	174	54.5	701	49.4	144	62.3	142	42.9
Moderate	147	26.7	591	33.8	79	24.8	492	34.7	37	16.0	130	39.3
Intemperate	11	2.0	173	9.9	9	2.8	140	9.9	2	0.9	33	10.0
Unascertained	74	13.4	141	8.1	57	17.9	84	5.9	48	20.8	26	7.9
Total	550	100.0	1748	100.0	319	100.0	1417	100.0	231	100.0	331	100.0

Summary

Jews have a higher rate of first admissions with psychoneuroses than non-Jews.

PART X

General Summary

IN the literature of the subject, it has been generally maintained that Jews have a higher incidence of mental disease than non-Jews, with the notable exception of the alcoholic psychoses. Those holding contrary views have agreed, nevertheless, that Jews have excessive rates with respect to some functional disorders, especially psychoneuroses. They attributed this to a variety of environmental factors, explicable on historical grounds. These are all hypothetical, and cannot be put to the test of empirical verification. Since few, if any, of the early studies of mental disease among Jews had real statistical validity, it seemed desirable to put the subject on as firm a statistical base as possible.

This study presents statistics of the incidence of mental disease among Jews and white non-Jews in New York State and New York City based upon first admissions to all mental hospitals in New York State during fiscal years 1939-1941, inclusive. There were 6987 Jewish and 35,576 non-Jewish first admissions during these years.

Eight groups of mental disorders included 87 per cent of the total Jewish first admissions. These may be divided into two categories: psychoses of organic origin, including general paresis, alcoholic psychoses, psychoses with cerebral arteriosclerosis, senile psychoses; and another group, called functional, including involutional psychoses, manic-depressive psychoses, dementia praecox, and psychoneuroses. The organic group included 27.2 per cent of total Jewish first admissions, and the functional group included 59.8 per cent. The same group of disorders included 83.7 per cent of total non-Jewish white first admissions. They were divided almost equally between the organic and the functional groups. The former included 42.9 per cent of the total, the latter included 40.8 per cent.

There is a fundamental difference between Jews and non-Jews with respect to the distribution of the groups of disorders. Among Jews, the chance of developing a functional disorder is more than twice that of developing a mental disorder of organic origin, whereas the chances are almost equal among non-Jews. Comparing Jews and non-Jews, directly, we find that the chance of non-Jewish first admissions belonging to the organic group of psychoses is about 50 per cent greater than the corresponding chance for Jewish first admissions. On the other hand, their chance of belonging to a functional group of disorders is a third less than that for Jewish first admissions.

Among Jews, the largest group of first admissions was dementia praecox, which included 30.8 per cent of the total. This was followed by psychoses with cerebral arteriosclerosis, with 16.2 per cent, and manic-depressive psychoses with 12.2 per cent. General paresis included only 2.8 per cent. Alcoholic psychoses were still lower with only 0.6 per cent.

Dementia praecox was also the leading category among non-Jews, but it included only 22.4 per cent of the total, compared with 30.8 per cent for Jews. Psychoses with cerebral arteriosclerosis and senile psychoses included 18.5 and 11.3 per cent, respectively, compared with corresponding percentages of 16.2 and 7.6 for Jews. The alcoholic psychoses included 7.4 per cent of non-Jewish first admissions, as against 0.6 per cent for Jews. General paresis included 5.7 per cent of non-Jewish admissions, compared with 2.8 per cent of Jews.

However, these are all proportional differences within the ranks of total first admissions of Jewish and non-Jewish origin, and do not give the probability of developing a mental disorder, as measured by *rates* of first admissions. The latter requires a ratio between the number of first admissions and the population from whom they were derived. This is usually expressed as the number of first admissions per 100,000 corresponding general population.

It is therefore necessary to relate Jewish first admissions to the general Jewish population. The latter, in turn, required a classification according to age. The manner in which these were estimated is given in detail in Part I. Corresponding data for non-Jews was obtained by subtracting totals for Jews from corresponding totals for the total white population.

Jews had an average annual rate of 105.6 per 100,000 population, compared with 111.1 for non-Jews. Because Jews are preponderantly inhabitants of New York City, it was necessary to make a further comparison, in which degree of urbanization was, for practical purposes, held constant. The general population for New York City was obtained in the manner explained in Part I. On this basis, Jews had a rate of 104.9, and non-Jews, 132.1. The rates for New York City were standardized with respect to age, resulting in rates of 136.7 per 100,000 Jews and 168.4 per 100,000 non-Jews.

It is evident, therefore, that the over-all rate of first admissions with mental disease was less for Jews than for non-Jews. This, and the remaining comparisons should be considered in connection with the fact that the Jewish population was undoubtedly underestimated. This increased the rate for Jews, and decreased correspondingly the rate for non-Jews. Therefore the correct differences in rates must be even greater than that shown above.

Similar comparisons were made with respect to eight groups of mental disorders. Four were of organic origin, and in each group the average annual rate of first admissions per 100,000 population was less for Jews.

For New York State, the rates for general paresis were 3.0 and 6.4 for Jews and non-Jews, respectively. When limited to New York City, the rates were 3.0 and 7.4, respectively. A further correction for New York City, gave standardized rates of 3.9 and 9.2, respectively.

Comparative rates for alcoholic psychoses have always created the greatest interest. The rate for Jews continued to be extraordinarily low among Jews, amounting to 0.6 for Jews, compared with 8.3 for non-Jews. Limiting the comparison to New York City, the rates were 0.7 and 12.2 for Jews and non-Jews, respectively. Standardizing the latter rates for age, they become 0.9 and 16.9, respectively.

We may summarize, next, the rates for those psychoses associated with advanced age. For New York State, the average annual rates for psychoses with cerebral arteriosclerosis were 17.1 for Jews and 20.6 for non-Jews. In New York City, the corresponding rates were 17.6 and 25.8. Because of the limited age range of the available data, it was not feasible to standardize, but it may be noted that among those aged 65 and over the rates were 199.5 for Jews and 258.0 for non-Jews.

In the case of the senile psychoses, the rates were 8.0 for Jews and 12.6 for non-Jews. For New York City, the corresponding rates were 8.2 and 13.8. At ages 65 and over, the rates were 148.7 for Jews and 214.2 for non-Jews.

We may consider next the four groups of functional mental disorders. For two, the rates for Jews were definitely greater than for non-Jews. With respect to manic-depressive psychoses, Jews had a rate of 12.9, non-Jews, 7.9. The relative order remained when the comparison was limited to New York City. The rates became 12.3 and 8.1, respectively. When standardized, the rates in New York City became 14.8 for Jews, and 9.8 for non-Jews.

Jews had a similar excess with respect to psychoneuroses. This should be considered in connection with the fact that admissions with psychoneuroses to mental hospitals are not a complete index, especially for Jews, who are more likely than non-Jews to seek private treatment for such disorders. In New York State, the rate for Jews was 8.3, compared with 5.4 for non-Jews. When standardized for age, the rates were 10.0 and 6.9, respectively. Corresponding data were not available for New York City, but it is highly probable that the differential between Jews and non-Jews is even greater in New York City.

In New York State, the rates for involutional psychoses were 9.4 for Jews and 7.1 for non-Jews. In New York City, however, the corresponding rates were 9.3 and 9.1. When standardized, the rates in New York City became 20.4 for Jews and 20.0 for non-Jews. Proper estimates of the Jewish population would probably reduce the rate for Jews by as much as 10 per cent, and increase that for non-Jews. Under the circumstances, a proper conclusion is that Jews and non-Jews do not differ significantly with respect to the relative frequency of involutional psychoses.

We come finally to dementia praecox, the largest of the categories of mental disease. For the State as a whole, Jews and non-Jews had rates of 32.5 and 24.9, respectively. For New York City, however, the corresponding rates were 32.8 and 32.2, and when standardized for age, they became 39.0 and 38.8, respectively. As with involutional psychoses, a better estimate of the Jewish general population would decrease the rate for Jews. But again, we adopt the conservative conclusion that there is no significant difference in such rates between Jews and non-Jews.

We have reviewed some basic data with respect to the frequency of mental disease among Jews. These statistics were derived from a systematic collection of data for the large aggregation of Jews in highly urbanized New York State and in the great metropolis of New York City. There may be some disputes as to the validity of first admissions as a complete measure of the incidence of mental disease. But their superiority over any other measure now available cannot be denied. Furthermore, the degree of incompleteness is relative, and there is no reason for believing it greater for Jews than for non-Jews. We shall leave to the future, attempts to unravel the social and psychological factors that may be basic to the question of differences in mental disease between Jews and any other ethnic group. In the light of the evidence in this study, it must be concluded that the differences are not in the quantitative direction that has been implied in the past, but rather along qualitative lines that require further investigation.

PART XI

Statistical Appendix

TABLE 87—Native Jewish first admissions to all hospitals for mental disease in New York State, 1939-1941, classified according to age.

Age (years)	Number			Per cent		
	Males	Females	Total	Males	Females	Total
Under 10	31	8	39	2.1	0.5	1.2
10–14	39	18	57	2.6	1.1	1.8
15–19	253	191	444	16.8	11.8	14.2
20–24	296	297	593	19.6	18.3	18.9
25–29	225	310	535	14.9	19.1	17.1
30–34	192	249	441	12.7	15.4	14.1
35–39	136	156	292	9.0	9.6	9.3
40–44	122	111	233	8.1	6.8	7.4
45–49	59	99	158	3.9	6.1	5.0
50–54	53	46	99	3.5	2.8	3.2
55–59	33	38	71	2.2	2.3	2.3
60–64	19	24	43	1.3	1.5	1.4
65–69	20	21	41	1.3	1.3	1.3
70–74	11	21	32	0.7	1.3	1.0
75–79	11	21	32	0.7	1.3	1.0
80–84	7	9	16	0.4	0.6	0.5
85–89	2	3	5	0.1	0.2	0.2
Total	1509	1622	3131	100.0	100.0	100.0

TABLE 88—Native non-Jewish white first admissions to all hospitals for mental disease in New York State, 1939-1941, classified according to age.

Age (years)	Number			Per cent		
	Males	Females	Total	Males	Females	Total
Under 10	68	26	94	0.5	0.2	0.4
10–14	108	67	175	0.8	0.6	0.7
15–19	595	514	1109	4.6	4.4	4.5
20–24	1130	910	2040	8.8	7.9	8.4
25–29	1191	1148	2339	9.2	10.0	9.6
30–34	1270	1090	2360	9.9	9.4	9.7
35–39	1283	1037	2320	10.0	9.0	9.5
40–44	1164	944	2108	9.0	8.2	8.6
45–49	1068	905	1973	8.3	7.9	8.1
50–54	1000	847	1847	7.8	7.4	7.6
55–59	741	658	1399	5.7	5.7	5.7
60–64	755	678	1433	5.9	5.9	5.9
65–69	749	738	1487	5.8	6.4	6.1
70–74	639	661	1300	5.0	5.7	5.3
75–79	598	625	1223	4.6	5.4	5.0
80–84	363	432	795	2.8	3.8	3.3
85–89	137	182	319	1.1	1.6	1.3
90 and over	31	47	78	0.2	0.4	0.3
Total	12890	11509	24399	100.0	100.0	100.0

TABLE 89—Foreign-born Jewish first admissions to all hospitals for mental disease in New York State, 1939-1941, classified according to age.

Age (years)	Number			Per cent		
	Males	Females	Total	Males	Females	Total
10–14	1	—	1	0.1	—	*
15–19	16	12	28	1.0	0.5	0.7
20–24	40	27	67	2.6	1.2	1.7
25–29	70	86	156	4.6	3.7	4.0
30–34	94	123	217	6.1	5.3	5.6
35–39	93	203	296	6.1	8.7	7.7
40–44	127	223	350	8.3	9.6	9.1
45–49	138	263	401	9.0	11.3	10.4
50–54	171	278	449	11.1	12.0	11.6
55–59	164	227	391	10.7	9.8	10.1
60–64	143	218	361	9.3	9.4	9.4
65–69	153	205	358	10.0	8.8	9.3
70–74	140	180	320	9.1	7.8	8.3
75–79	104	140	244	6.8	6.0	6.3
80–84	48	89	137	3.1	3.8	3.6
85–89	24	29	53	1.6	1.2	1.4
90 and over	8	19	27	0.5	0.8	0.7
Total	1534	2322	3856	100.0	100.0	100.0

*Less than 0.05.

TABLE 90—Foreign-born non-Jewish white first admissions to all hospitals for mental disease in New York State, 1939-1941, classified according to age.

Age (years)	Number			Per cent		
	Males	Females	Total	Males	Females	Total
10–14	1	2	3	*	*	*
15–19	41	29	70	0.7	0.6	0.6
20–24	72	55	127	1.2	1.1	1.1
25–29	137	148	285	2.2	3.0	2.5
30–34	260	284	544	4.2	5.7	4.9
35–39	433	422	855	7.0	8.7	7.7
40–44	591	408	999	9.5	8.2	8.9
45–49	659	479	1138	10.6	9.7	10.2
50–54	749	503	1252	12.0	10.2	11.2
55–59	661	403	1064	10.6	8.1	9.5
60–64	622	416	1038	10.0	8.4	9.3
65–69	569	432	1001	9.1	8.7	9.0
70–74	529	449	978	8.5	9.1	8.8
75–79	450	421	871	7.2	8.5	7.8
80–84	297	296	593	4.8	6.0	5.3
85–89	113	161	274	1.8	3.2	2.4
90 and over	38	47	85	0.6	0.9	0.8
Total	6222	4955	11177	100.0	100.0	100.0

*Less than 0.05.

TABLE 91—Native Jewish first admissions to all hospitals for mental disease in New York State, 1939–1941, classified according to nativity of parents and environment.

Nativity of parents	Total			Urban												Rural								
				Total			New York City			Other			Total			Farm			Non-farm		
	M	F	T	M	F	T	M	F	T	M	F	T	M	F	T	M	F	T	M	F	T
Number																					
Russia	699	772	1471	694	765	1459	637	700	1337	57	65	122	5	7	12	1	—	1	4	7	11
Poland	144	163	307	142	163	305	120	135	255	22	28	50	2	—	2	1	—	1	1	—	1
Austria	211	245	456	210	245	455	200	236	436	10	9	19	1	—	1	1	—	1	—	—	—
Germany	87	107	194	87	105	192	78	90	168	9	15	24	—	2	2	—	—	—	—	2	2
Hungary	50	60	110	50	60	110	48	57	105	2	3	5	—	—	—	—	—	—	—	—	—
Roumania	56	68	124	56	68	124	48	61	109	8	7	15	—	—	—	—	—	—	—	—	—
All native-born	1509	1622	3131	1497	1610	3107	1342	1465	2807	155	145	300	12	12	24	3	—	3	9	12	21
Per cent																					
Russia	100.0	100.0	100.0	99.3	99.1	99.2	91.1	90.7	90.1	8.2	8.4	8.3	0.7	0.9	0.8	0.1	—	0.1	0.6	0.9	0.7
Poland	100.0	100.0	100.0	98.6	100.0	99.3	83.3	82.8	83.1	15.3	17.2	16.3	1.4	—	0.7	0.7	—	0.3	0.7	—	0.3
Austria	100.0	100.0	100.0	99.5	100.0	99.8	94.8	96.3	95.6	4.7	3.7	4.2	0.4	—	0.2	0.4	—	0.2	—	—	—
Germany	100.0	100.0	100.0	100.0	98.1	99.0	89.7	84.1	86.6	10.3	14.0	12.4	—	1.9	1.0	—	—	—	—	1.9	1.0
Hungary	100.0	100.0	100.0	100.0	100.0	100.0	96.0	95.0	95.5	4.0	5.0	4.5	—	—	—	—	—	—	—	—	—
Russia	100.0	100.0	100.0	100.0	100.0	100.0	85.7	89.7	87.9	14.3	10.3	12.1	—	—	—	—	—	—	—	—	—
All native-born	100.0	100.0	100.0	99.2	99.3	99.2	88.9	90.3	89.7	10.3	8.9	9.6	0.8	0.7	0.8	0.2	—	0.1	0.6	0.7	0.7

Table 92—Native Jewish first admissions to all hospitals for mental disease in New York State, 1939–1941, classified according to nativity of parents and use of alcohol.

Nativity of parents	Total			Abstinent			Moderate			Intemperate			Unascertained		
	M	F	T	M	F	T	M	F	T	M	F	T	M	F	T
Number															
Russia	699	772	1471	468	632	1100	157	86	243	35	5	40	39	49	88
Poland	144	163	307	103	135	238	32	22	54	5	—	5	4	6	10
Austria	211	245	456	120	195	315	68	36	104	2	—	2	21	14	35
Germany	87	107	194	49	86	135	27	21	48	6	—	6	5	—	5
Hungary	50	60	110	27	48	75	20	6	26	2	—	2	1	6	7
Roumania	56	68	124	37	47	84	19	9	28	—	3	3	—	9	9
All native-born	1509	1622	3131	963	1304	2267	399	222	621	67	9	76	80	87	167
Per cent															
Russia	100.0	100.0	100.0	67.0	81.9	74.8	22.4	11.1	16.5	5.0	0.6	2.7	5.6	6.3	6.0
Poland	100.0	100.0	100.0	71.5	82.8	77.5	22.2	13.5	17.6	3.4	—	1.6	2.8	3.7	3.3
Austria	100.0	100.0	100.0	56.9	79.6	69.1	32.2	14.7	22.8	0.9	—	0.4	10.0	5.7	7.7
Germany	100,0	100.0	100.0	56.3	80.4	69..6	31.0	19.6	24.7	6.9	—	3.1	5.7	—	2.6
Hungary	100.0	100.0	100.0	54.0	80.0	68.2	40.0	10.0	23.6	4.0	—	1.8	2.0	10.0	6.4
Roumania	100.0	100.0	100.0	66.1	69.1	67.7	33.9	13.2	22.6	—	4.4	2.4	—	13.2	7.3
All native-born	100.0	100.0	100.0	63.8	80.4	72.4	26.4	13.7	19.8	4.4	0.6	2.4	5.3	5.4	5.3

TABLE 93—Foreign-born Jewish first admissions to all hospitals for mental disease in New York State, 1939–1941, classified according to nativity and environment.

Nativity of parents	Total			Urban									Rural								
				Total			New York City			Other			Total			Farm			Non-farm		
	M	F	T	M	F	T	M	F	T	M	F	T	M	F	T	M	F	T	M	F	T
	Number																				
Russia	709	1108	1817	707	1105	1812	660	1036	1696	47	69	116	2	3	5	1	1	2	1	2	3
Poland	273	354	627	272	353	625	254	325	579	18	28	46	1	1	2	—	—	—	1	1	2
Austria	215	349	564	215	348	563	207	341	548	8	7	15	—	1	1	—	—	—	—	1	1
Germany	91	139	230	89	139	228	72	134	206	17	5	22	2	—	2	—	—	—	2	—	2
Hungary	68	128	196	64	127	191	61	126	187	3	1	4	4	1	5	1	—	1	3	1	4
Roumania	52	89	141	52	88	140	51	85	136	1	3	4	—	1	1	—	—	—	—	1	1
All foreign-born	1534	2322	3856	1525	2315	3840	1414	2184	3598	111	131	242	9	7	16	2	1	3	7	6	13
	Per cent																				
Russia	100.0	100.0	100.0	99.7	99.7	99.7	93.1	93.5	93.3	6.6	6.2	6.4	0.3	0.3	0.3	0.1	0.1	0.1	0.1	0.2	0.2
Poland	100.0	100.0	100.0	99.6	99.7	99.7	93.0	91.8	92.3	6.6	7.9	7.3	0.4	0.3	0.3	—	—	—	0.4	0.3	0.3
Austria	100.0	100.0	100.0	100.0	99.7	99.8	96.3	97.7	97.2	3.7	2.0	2.7	—	0.3	0.2	—	—	—	—	0.3	0.2
Germany	100.0	100.0	100.0	97.8	100.0	99.1	79.1	96.4	89.6	18.7	3.6	9.6	2.2	—	0.9	—	—	—	2.2	—	0.9
Hungary	100.0	100.0	100.0	94.1	99.2	97.4	89.7	98.4	95.4	4.4	0.8	2.0	5.9	0.8	2.6	1.5	—	0.5	4.4	0.8	2.0
Roumania	100.0	100.0	100.0	100.0	98.9	99.3	98.1	95.5	96.4	1.9	3.4	2.8	—	1.1	0.7	—	—	—	—	1.1	0.7
All foreign-born	100.0	100.0	100.0	99.4	99.7	99.6	92.2	94.1	93.3	7.2	5.6	6.3	0.6	0.3	0.4	0.1	*	0.1	0.5	0.3	0.3

* Less than 0.05

TABLE 94—Foreign-born Jewish first admissions to all hospitals for mental disease in New York State, 1939–1941, classified according to nativity and use of alcohol.

Nativity of parents	Total			Abstinent			Moderate			Intemperate			Unascertained		
	M	F	T	M	F	T	M	F	T	M	F	T	M	F	T
Number															
Russia	709	1108	1817	427	985	1412	201	67	268	45	7	52	36	49	85
Poland	273	354	627	179	312	491	74	31	105	8	—	8	12	11	23
Austria	215	349	564	126	306	432	70	23	93	17	1	18	2	19	21
Germany	91	139	230	42	105	147	36	27	63	1	3	4	12	4	16
Hungary	68	128	196	45	96	141	20	29	49	3	—	3	—	3	3
Roumania	52	89	141	26	83	109	20	5	25	3	—	3	3	1	4
All foreign-born	1534	2322	3856	910	2019	2929	444	199	643	85	14	99	95	90	185
Per cent															
Russia	100.0	100.0	100.0	60.2	88.9	77.7	28.3	6.0	14.7	6.4	0.6	2.9	5.1	4.4	4.7
Poland	100.0	100.0	100.0	65.6	88.1	78.3	27.1	8.8	16.7	2.9	—	1.3	4.4	3.1	3.7
Austria	100.0	100.0	100.0	58.6	87.7	76.6	32.6	6.6	16.5	7.9	0.3	3.2	0.9	5.4	3.7
Germany	100.0	100.0	100.0	46.2	75.5	63.9	39.6	19.4	27.4	1.1	2.2	1.7	13.2	2.9	7.0
Hungary	100.0	100.0	100.0	66.2	75.0	71.9	29.4	22.7	25.0	4.4	—	1.5	—	2.3	1.5
Roumania	100.0	100.0	100.0	50.0	93.3	77.3	38.4	5.6	17.7	5.8	—	2.1	5.8	1.1	2.8
All foreign-born	100.0	100.0	100.0	59.3	87.0	76.0	28.9	8.6	16.7	5.5	0.6	2.6	6.2	3.9	4.8

TABLE 95—Foreign-born Jewish first admissions to all hospitals for mental disease in New York State, 1939–1941, classified according to nativity and time in United States prior to admission.

Nativity	Total			Less than 1 year			1 to 4 years			5 to 9 years			10 to 14 years			15 years and over			Unascertained		
	M	F	T	M	F	T	M	F	T	M	F	T	M	F	T	M	F	T	M	F	T
										Number											
Russia	709	1108	1817	9	6	15	10	11	21	13	13	26	23	34	57	643	1023	1666	11	21	32
Poland	273	354	627	4	4	8	9	7	16	15	10	25	28	33	61	215	297	512	2	3	5
Austria	215	349	564	11	15	26	11	14	25	2	5	7	7	8	15	181	306	487	3	1	4
Germany	91	139	230	7	24	31	25	31	56	5	5	10	2	6	8	51	68	119	1	5	6
Hungary	68	128	196	—	4	4	2	7	9	2	2	4	1	7	8	63	105	168	—	3	3
Roumania	52	89	141	4	4	8	1	—	1	—	—	—	1	4	5	46	81	127	—	—	—
All foreign-born	1534	2322	3856	43	63	106	71	75	146	40	42	82	73	108	181	1287	2001	3288	20	33	53
										Per cent											
Russia	100.0	100.0	100.0	1.3	0.5	0.8	1.4	1.0	1.2	1.8	1.2	1.4	3.2	3.1	3.1	90.7	92.3	91.7	1.6	1.9	1.8
Poland	100.0	100.0	100.0	1.4	1.1	1.3	3.3	2.0	2.6	5.5	2.8	4.0	10.3	9.3	9.7	78.8	83.9	81.7	0.7	0.8	0.8
Austria	100.0	100.0	100.0	5.1	4.3	4.6	5.1	4.0	4.4	0.9	1.4	1.2	3.3	2.3	2.7	84.2	87.7	86.4	1.4	0.3	0.7
Germany	100.0	100.0	100.0	7.7	17.3	13.5	27.4	22.3	24.3	5.5	3.6	4.3	2.2	4.3	3.5	56.0	48.9	51.7	1.1	3.6	2.6
Hungary	100.0	100.0	100.0	—	3.1	2.0	2.9	5.5	4.6	2.9	1.6	2.0	1.4	5.5	4.1	92.7	82.0	85.7	—	2.3	1.5
Roumania	100.0	100.0	100.0	7.7	4.5	5.7	1.9	—	0.7	—	—	—	1.9	4.5	3.5	88.4	91.0	90.1	—	—	—
All foreign-born	100.0	100.0	100.0	2.8	2.7	2.7	4.6	3.2	3.8	2.6	1.8	2.1	4.8	4.7	4.7	83.9	86.2	85.3	1.3	1.4	1.4

TABLE 96—Native Jewish first admissions with general paresis to all hospitals for mental disease in New York State, 1939-1941, classified according to age.

Age (years)	Number			Per cent		
	Males	Females	Total	Males	Females	Total
20–24	2	—	2	3.6	—	2.9
25–29	1	2	3	1.8	13.3	4.3
30–34	7	3	10	12.7	20.0	14.3
35–39	7	4	11	12.7	26.7	15.7
40–44	10	—	10	18.2	—	14.3
45–49	8	3	11	14.6	20.0	15.7
50–54	6	2	8	10.9	13.3	11.4
55–59	7	—	7	12.7	—	10.0
60–64	2	—	2	3.6	—	2.9
65–69	1	1	2	1.8	6.7	2.9
70–74	2	—	2	3.6	—	2.9
75–79	2	—	2	3.6	—	2.9
Total	55	15	70	100.0	100.0	100.0

TABLE 97—Native non-Jewish white first admissions with general paresis to all hospitals for mental disease in New York State, 1939-1941, classified according to age.

Age (years)	Number			Per cent		
	Males	Females	Total	Males	Females	Total
5–9	—	1	1	—	0.3	0.1
10–14	6	1	7	0.7	0.3	0.6
15–19	6	9	15	0.7	2.4	1.2
20–24	5	9	14	0.6	2.4	1.1
25–29	25	26	51	2.8	7.0	4.1
30–34	108	49	157	12.2	13.2	12.5
35–39	151	65	216	17.1	17.6	17.2
40–44	149	63	212	16.9	17.0	16.9
45–49	140	47	187	15.9	12.7	14.9
50–54	125	38	163	14.2	10.3	13.0
55–59	75	28	103	8.4	7.6	8.2
60–64	48	17	65	5.4	4.6	5.2
65–69	27	11	38	3.1	3.0	3.0
70–74	8	4	12	0.9	1.1	1.0
75–79	9	1	10	1.0	0.3	0.8
80–84	1	—	1	0.1	—	0.1
85–89	—	1	1	—	0.3	0.1
Total	883	370	1253	100.0	100.0	100.0

TABLE 98—Foreign-born Jewish first admissions with general paresis to all hospitals for mental disease in New York State, 1939-1941, classified according to age.

Age (years)	Number			Per cent		
	Males	Females	Total	Males	Females	Total
25–29	—	1	1	—	2.8	0.8
30–34	2	—	2	2.2	—	1.6
35–39	7	3	10	7.7	8.3	7.9
40–44	19	5	24	20.9	13.9	18.9
45–49	17	4	21	18.7	11.1	16.5
50–54	13	6	19	14.3	16.7	15.0
55–59	12	6	18	13.2	16.7	14.2
60–64	10	7	17	11.0	19.4	13.4
65–69	9	1	10	9.9	2.8	7.9
70–74	2	2	4	2.2	5.6	3.1
75–79	—	1	1	—	2.8	0.8
Total	91	36	127	100.0	100.0	100.0

TABLE 99—Foreign-born non-Jewish first admissions with general paresis to all hospitals for mental disease in New York State, 1939-1941, classified according to age.

Age (years)	Number			Per cent		
	Males	Females	Total	Males	Females	Total
15–19	—	4	4	—	3.3	0.5
20–24	—	—	—	—	—	—
25–29	8	1	9	1.2	0.8	1.1
30–34	20	10	30	3.0	8.3	3.8
35–39	67	17	84	10.0	14.2	10.6
40–44	135	17	152	20.1	14.2	19.2
45–49	124	19	143	18.5	15.8	18.1
50–55	129	18	147	19.3	15.0	18.6
55–59	79	12	91	11.8	10.0	11.5
60–64	50	9	59	7.4	7.5	7.5
65–69	36	6	42	5.4	5.0	5.3
70–74	12	4	16	1.8	3.3	2.0
75–79	8	3	11	1.2	2.5	1.4
80–84	2	—	2	0.3	—	0.3
Total	670	120	790	100.0	100.0	100.0

Table 100—Native Jewish first admissions with general paresis to all hospitals for mental disease in New York State, 1939–1941, classified according to nativity of parents and environment.

Nativity of parents	Total			Urban									Rural								
				Total			New York City			Other			Total			Farm			Non-farm		
	M	F	T	M	F	T	M	F	T	M	F	T	M	F	T	M	F	T	M	F	T
Number																					
Russia	20	4	24	20	4	24	17	3	20	3	1	4	—	—	—	—	—	—	—	—	—
Poland	3	1	4	3	1	4	2	1	3	1	—	1	—	—	—	—	—	—	—	—	—
Austria	5	2	7	5	2	7	5	2	7	—	—	—	—	—	—	—	—	—	—	—	—
Germany	7	4	11	7	4	11	6	4	10	1	—	1	—	—	—	—	—	—	—	—	—
Hungary	5	2	7	5	2	7	5	2	7	—	—	—	—	—	—	—	—	—	—	—	—
Roumania	2	—	2	2	—	2	2	—	2	—	—	—	—	—	—	—	—	—	—	—	—
All native-born	55	15	70	55	15	70	49	14	63	6	1	7	—	—	—	—	—	—	—	—	—
Per cent																					
Russia	100.0	100.0	100.0	100.0	100.0	100.0	85.0	75.0	83.3	15.0	25.0	16.7	—	—	—	—	—	—	—	—	—
Poland	100.0	100.0	100.0	100.0	100.0	100.0	66.7	100.0	75.0	33.3	—	25.0	—	—	—	—	—	—	—	—	—
Austria	100.0	100.0	100.0	100.0	100.0	100.0	100.0	100.0	100.0	—	—	—	—	—	—	—	—	—	—	—	—
Germany	100.0	100.0	100.0	100.0	100.0	100.0	85.7	100.0	90.9	14.3	—	9.1	—	—	—	—	—	—	—	—	—
Hungary	100.0	100.0	100.0	100.0	100.0	100.0	100.0	100.0	100.0	—	—	—	—	—	—	—	—	—	—	—	—
Roumania	100.0	—	100.0	100.0	—	100.0	100.0	—	100.0	—	—	—	—	—	—	—	—	—	—	—	—
All native-born	100.0	100.0	100.0	100.0	100.0	100.0	89.1	93.3	90.0	10.9	6.7	10.0	—	—	—	—	—	—	—	—	—

TABLE 101—Native Jewish first admissions with general paresis to all hospitals for mental disease in New York State, 1939–1941, classified according to nativity of parents and use of alcohol.

Nativity of parents	Total			Abstinent			Moderate			Intemperate			Unascertained		
	M	F	T	M	F	T	M	F	T	M	F	T	M	F	T
							Number								
Russia	20	4	24	9	3	12	9	—	9	2	1	3	—	—	—
Poland	3	1	4	2	1	3	1	—	1	—	—	—	—	—	—
Austria	5	2	7	2	2	4	2	—	2	1	—	1	—	—	—
Germany	7	4	11	3	4	7	4	—	4	—	—	—	—	—	—
Hungary	5	2	7	4	2	6	1	—	1	—	—	—	—	—	—
Roumania	2	—	2	1	—	1	1	—	1	—	—	—	—	—	—
All native-born	55	15	70	25	13	38	27	1	28	3	1	4	—	—	—
							Per cent								
Russia	100.0	100.0	100.0	45.0	75.0	50.0	45.0	—	37.5	10.0	25.0	12.5	—	—	—
Poland	100.0	100.0	100.0	66.7	100.0	75.0	33.3	—	25.0	—	—	—	—	—	—
Austria	100.0	100.0	100.0	40.0	100.0	57.1	40.0	—	28.6	20.0	—	14.3	—	—	—
Germany	100.0	100.0	100.0	42.9	100.0	63.6	57.1	—	36.4	—	—	—	—	—	—
Hungary	100.0	100.0	100.0	80.0	100.0	85.7	20.0	—	14.3	—	—	—	—	—	—
Roumania	100.0	—	100.0	50.0	—	50.0	50.0	—	50.0	—	—	—	—	—	—
All native-born	100.0	100.0	100.0	45.4	86.7	54.3	49.1	6.7	40.0	5.5	6.7	5.7	—	—	—

TABLE 102—Foreign-born Jewish first admissions with general paresis to all hospitals for mental disease in New York State, 1939–1941, classified according to nativity and environment.

Nativity of parents	Total			Urban									Rural								
				Total			New York City			Other			Total			Farm			Non-farm		
	M	F	T	M	F	T	M	F	T	M	F	T	M	F	T	M	F	T	M	F	T
Number																					
Russia	40	10	50	40	10	50	37	10	47	3	—	3	—	—	—	—	—	—	—	—	—
Poland	16	7	23	16	7	23	16	7	23	—	—	—	—	—	—	—	—	—	—	—	—
Austria	6	8	14	6	8	14	5	7	12	1	1	2	—	—	—	—	—	—	—	—	—
Germany	8	—	8	8	—	8	7	—	7	1	—	1	—	—	—	—	—	—	—	—	—
Hungary	6	4	10	6	4	10	6	4	10	—	—	—	—	—	—	—	—	—	—	—	—
Roumania	10	3	13	10	3	13	10	3	13	—	—	—	—	—	—	—	—	—	—	—	—
All foreign-born	91	36	127	91	36	127	86	34	120	5	2	7	—	—	—	—	—	—	—	—	—
Per cent																					
Russia	100.0	100.0	100.0	100.0	100.0	100.0	92.5	100.0	94.0	7.5	—	6.0	—	—	—	—	—	—	—	—	—
Poland	100.0	100.0	100.0	100.0	100.0	100.0	100.0	100.0	100.0	—	—	—	—	—	—	—	—	—	—	—	—
Austria	100.0	100.0	100.0	100.0	100.0	100.0	83.3	87.5	85.7	16.7	12.5	14.3	—	—	—	—	—	—	—	—	—
Germany	100.0	—	100.0	100.0	—	100.0	87.5	—	87.5	12.5	—	12.5	—	—	—	—	—	—	—	—	—
Hungary	100.0	100.0	100.0	100.0	100.0	100.0	100.0	100.0	100.0	—	—	—	—	—	—	—	—	—	—	—	—
Roumania	100.0	100.0	100.0	100.0	100.0	100.0	100.0	100.0	100.0	—	—	—	—	—	—	—	—	—	—	—	—
All foreign-born	100.0	100.0	100.0	100.0	100.0	100.0	94.5	94.4	94.5	5.5	5.6	5.5	—	—	—	—	—	—	—	—	—

TABLE 103—Foreign-born Jewish first admissions with general paresis to all hospitals for mental disease in New York State, 1939–1941, classified according to nativity and use of alcohol.

Nativity of parents	Total			Abstinent			Moderate			Intemperate			Unascertained		
	M	F	T	M	F	T	M	F	T	M	F	T	M	F	T
Number															
Russia	40	10	50	16	9	25	21	1	22	3	—	3	—	—	—
Poland	16	7	23	12	7	19	4	—	4	—	—	—	—	—	—
Austria	6	8	14	4	5	9	2	3	5	—	—	—	—	—	—
Germany	8	—	8	1	—	1	7	—	7	—	—	—	—	—	—
Hungary	6	4	10	2	2	4	4	2	6	—	—	—	—	—	—
Roumania	10	3	13	6	3	9	3	—	3	1	—	1	—	—	—
All foreign-born	91	36	127	48	28	76	38	8	46	5	—	5	—	—	—
Per cent															
Russia	100.0	100.0	100.0	40.0	90.0	50.0	52.5	10.0	44.0	7.5	—	6.0	—	—	—
Poland	100.0	100.0	100.0	66.7	100.0	82.6	33.3	—	17.4	—	—	—	—	—	—
Austria	100.0	100.0	100.0	66.7	62.5	64.3	33.3	37.5	35.7	—	—	—	—	—	—
Germany	100.0	—	100.0	12.5	—	12.5	87.5	—	87.5	—	—	—	—	—	—
Hungary	100.0	100.0	100.0	33.3	50.0	40.0	66.7	50.0	60.0	—	—	—	—	—	—
Roumania	100.0	100.0	100.0	60.0	100.0	69.2	30.0	—	23.1	10.0	—	7.6	—	—	—
All foreign-born	100.0	100.0	100.0	52.7	77.8	59.8	41.8	22.2	36.2	5.5	—	3.9	—	—	—

Table 104—Foreign-born Jewish first admissions with general paresis to all hospitals for mental disease in New York State, 1939–1941, classified according to nativity and time in United States prior to admission.

Nativity	Total			Less than 1 year			1 to 4 years			5 to 9 years			10 to 14 years			15 years and over			Unascertained		
	M	F	T	M	F	T	M	F	T	M	F	T	M	F	T	M	F	T	M	F	T
										Number											
Russia	40	10	50	1	—	1	—	—	—	1	—	1	2	—	2	36	10	46	—	—	—
Poland	16	7	23	—	—	—	—	—	—	2	—	2	4	—	4	10	7	17	—	—	—
Austria	6	8	14	—	—	—	1	—	1	—	—	—	—	—	—	5	8	13	—	—	—
Germany	8	—	8	—	—	—	3	—	3	—	—	—	2	—	2	3	—	3	—	—	—
Hungary	6	4	10	—	—	—	—	—	—	—	—	—	—	1	1	6	3	9	—	—	—
Roumania	10	3	13	—	—	—	—	—	—	—	—	—	—	—	—	10	3	13	—	—	—
All foreign-born	91	36	127	1	—	1	5	—	5	3	—	3	8	1	9	74	35	109	—	—	—
										Per cent											
Russia	100.0	100.0	100.0	2.5	—	2.0	—	—	—	2.5	—	2.0	5.0	—	4.0	90.0	100.0	92.0	—	—	—
Poland	100.0	100.0	100.0	—	—	—	—	—	—	12.5	—	8.7	25.0	—	17.4	62.5	100.0	73.9	—	—	—
Austria	100.0	100.0	100.0	—	—	—	16.7	—	7.1	—	—	—	—	—	—	83.3	100.0	92.9	—	—	—
Germany	100.0	—	100.0	—	—	—	37.5	—	37.5	—	—	—	25.0	—	25.0	37.5	—	37.5	—	—	—
Hungary	100.0	100.0	100.0	—	—	—	—	—	—	—	—	—	—	25.0	10.0	100.0	75.0	9.00	—	—	—
Roumania	100.0	100.0	100.0	—	—	—	—	—	—	—	—	—	—	—	—	100.0	100.0	100.0	—		—
All foreign-born	100.0	100.0	100.0	1.1	—	0.8	5.5	—	3.9	3.3	—	2.4	8.8	2.8	7.1	81.3	97.2	85.8	—	—	—

TABLE 105—Native Jewish first admissions with alcoholic psychoses to all hospitals for mental disease in New York State, 1939-1941, classified according to agc.

Age (years)	Number			Per cent		
	Males	Females	Total	Males	Females	Total
25–29	1	—	1	6.7	—	6.7
30–34	1	—	1	6.7	—	6.7
35–39	3	—	3	20.0	—	20.0
40–44	4	—	4	26.7	—	26.7
45–49	4	—	4	26.7	—	26.7
50–54	2	—	2	13.3	—	13.3
Total	15	—	15	100.0	—	100.0

TABLE 106—Native non-Jewish white first admissions with alcoholic psychoses to all hospitals for mental disease in New York State, 1939-1941, classified according to age.

Age (years)	Number			Per cent		
	Males	Females	Total	Males	Females	Total
20–24	12	2	14	0.8	0.7	0.8
25–29	72	24	96	4.7	8.9	5.4
30–34	166	48	214	10.9	17.8	11.9
35–39	278	40	318	18.3	14.9	17.8
40–44	269	36	305	17.7	13.4	17.0
45–49	243	37	280	16.0	13.8	15.6
50–54	217	40	257	14.3	14.9	14.3
55–59	115	18	133	7.6	6.7	7.4
60–64	82	18	100	5.4	6.7	5.6
65–69	55	4	59	3.6	1.5	3.3
70–74	8	2	10	0.5	0.7	0.6
75–79	5	—	5	0.3	—	0.3
Total	1522	269	1791	100.0	100.0	100.0

Table 107—Foreign-born Jewish first admissions with alcoholic psychoses to all hospitals for mental disease in New York State, 1939-1941, classified according to age.

Age (years)	Number			Per cent		
	Males	Females	Total	Males	Females	Total
30–34	1	—	1	4.4	—	3.7
35–39	1	3	4	4.4	75.0	14.8
40–44	—	—	—	—	—	—
45–49	7	—	7	30.4	—	25.9
50–54	5	—	5	21.7	—	18.5
55–59	5	1	6	21.7	25.0	27.2
60–64	4	—	4	17.4	—	14.8
Total	23	4	27	100.0	100.0	100.0

Table 108—Foreign-born non-Jewish white first admissions with alcoholic psychoses to all hospitals for mental disease in New York State, 1939-1941, classified according to age.

Age (years)	Number			Per cent		
	Males	Females	Total	Males	Females	Total
25–29	4	1	5	0.6	0.6	0.6
30–34	33	5	38	4.8	3.1	4.4
35–39	66	16	82	9.5	9.9	9.6
40–44	99	28	127	14.3	17.3	14.9
45–49	131	21	152	18.9	13.0	17.8
50–54	131	26	157	18.9	16.1	18.4
55–59	101	26	127	14.6	16.1	14.9
60–64	71	20	91	10.3	12.3	10.7
65–69	38	10	48	5.5	6.2	5.6
70–74	13	5	18	1.8	3.1	2.1
75–79	4	4	8	0.6	2.4	0.9
80–84	1	—	1	0.1	—	0.1
Total	692	162	854	100.0	100.0	100.0

TABLE 109—Native Jewish first admissions with alcoholic psychoses to all hospitals for mental disease in New York State, 1939–1941, classified according to nativity of parents and environment.

Nativity of parents	Total			Urban									Rural								
				Total			New York City			Other			Total			Farm			Non-farm		
	M	F	T	M	F	T	M	F	T	M	F	T	M	F	T	M	F	T	M	F	T
										Number											
Russia	10	—	10	10	—	10	10	—	10	—	—	—	—	—	—	—	—	—	—	—	—
Poland	1	—	1	1	—	1	1	—	1	—	—	—	—	—	—	—	—	—	—	—	—
Austria	—	—	—	—	—	—	—	—	—	—	—	—	—	—	—	—	—	—	—	—	—
Germany	1	—	1	1	—	1	1	—	1	—	—	—	—	—	—	—	—	—	—	—	—
Hungary	1	—	1	1	—	1	1	—	1	—	—	—	—	—	—	—	—	—	—	—	—
Roumania	—	—	—	—	—	—	—	—	—	—	—	—	—	—	—	—	—	—	—	—	—
All native-born	15	—	15	15	—	15	15	—	15	—	—	—	—	—	—	—	—	—	—	—	—
										Per cent											
Russia	100.0	—	100.0	100.0	—	100.0	100.0	—	100.0	—	—	—	—	—	—	—	—	—	—	—	—
Poland	100.0	—	100.0	100.0	—	100.0	100.0	—	100.0	—	—	—	—	—	—	—	—	—	—	—	—
Austria	—	—	—	—	—	—	—	—	—	—	—	—	—	—	—	—	—	—	—	—	—
Germany	100.0	—	100.0	100.0	—	100.0	100.0	—	100.0	—	—	—	—	—	—	—	—	—	—	—	—
Hungary	100.0	—	100.0	100.0	—	100.0	100.0	—	100.0	—	—	—	—	—	—	—	—	—	—	—	—
Roumania	—	—	—	—	—	—	—	—	—	—	—	—	—	—	—	—	—	—	—	—	—
All native-born	100.0	—	100.0	100.0	—	100.0	100.0	—	100.0	—	—	—	—	—	—	—	—	—	—	—	—

TABLE 110—Foreign-born Jewish first admissions with alcoholic psychoses to all hospitals for mental disease in New York State, 1939–1941, classified according to nativity and environment.

Nativity of parents	Total			Urban									Rural								
				Total			New York City			Other			Total			Farm			Non-farm		
	M	F	T	M	F	T	M	F	T	M	F	T	M	F	T	M	F	T	M	F	T
Number																					
Russia	11	—	11	11	—	11	11	—	11	—	—	—	—	—	—	—	—	—	—	—	—
Poland	3	3	6	3	3	6	3	3	6	—	—	—	—	—	—	—	—	—	—	—	—
Austria	3	—	3	3	—	3	3	—	3	—	—	—	—	—	—	—	—	—	—	—	—
Germany	—	—	—	—	—	—	—	—	—	—	—	—	—	—	—	—	—	—	—	—	—
Hungary	1	—	1	1	—	1	1	—	1	—	—	—	—	—	—	—	—	—	—	—	—
Roumania	—	—	—	—	—	—	—	—	—	—	—	—	—	—	—	—	—	—	—	—	—
All foreign-born	23	4	27	23	4	27	22	4	26	1	—	1	—	—	—	—	—	—	—	—	—
Per cent																					
Russia	100.0	—	100.0	100.0	—	100.0	100.0	—	100.0	—	—	—	—	—	—	—	—	—	—	—	—
Poland	100.0	100.0	100.0	100.0	100.0	100.0	100.0	100.0	100.0	—	—	—	—	—	—	—	—	—	—	—	—
Austria	100.0	—	100.0	100.0	—	100.0	100.0	—	100.0	—	—	—	—	—	—	—	—	—	—	—	—
Germany	—	—	—	—	—	—	—	—	—	—	—	—	—	—	—	—	—	—	—	—	—
Hungary	100.0	—	100.0	100.0	—	100.0	100.0	—	100.0	—	—	—	—	—	—	—	—	—	—	—	—
Roumania	—	—	—	—	—	—	—	—	—	—	—	—	—	—	—	—	—	—	—	—	—
All foreign-born	100.0	100.0	100.0	100.0	100.0	100.0	95.7	100.0	96.3	4.3	—	3.7	—	—	—	—	—	—	—	—	—

TABLE 111—Foreign-born Jewish first admissions with alcoholic psychoses to all hospitals for mental disease in New York State, 1939–1941, classified according to nativity and time in United States prior to admission.

Nativity	Total			Less than 1 year			1 to 4 years			5 to 9 years			10 to 14 years			15 years and over			Unascertained		
	M	F	T	M	F	T	M	F	T	M	F	T	M	F	T	M	F	T	M	F	T
										Number											
Russia	11	—	11	—	—	—	1	—	1	—	—	—	—	—	—	10	—	10	—	—	—
Poland	3	3	6	—	—	—	—	—	—	—	—	—	—	—	—	3	3	6	—	—	—
Austria	3	—	3	—	—	—	—	—	—	—	—	—	—	—	—	2	—	2	1	—	1
Germany	—	—	—	—	—	—	—	—	—	—	—	—	—	—	—	—	—	—	—	—	—
Hungary	1	—	1	—	—	—	—	—	—	—	—	—	—	—	—	1	—	1	—	—	—
Roumania	—	—	—	—	—	—	—	—	—	—	—	—	—	—	—	—	—	—	—	—	—
All foreign-born	23	4	27	—	—	—	1	—	1	—	—	—	—	—	—	21	4	25	1	—	1
										Per cent											
Russia	100.0	—	100.0	—	—	—	9.1	—	9.1	—	—	—	—	—	—	90.9	—	90.9	—	—	—
Poland	100.0	100.0	100.0	—	—	—	—	—	—	—	—	—	—	—	—	100.0	100.0	100.0	—	—	—
Austria	100.0	—	100.0	—	—	—	—	—	—	—	—	—	—	—	—	66.7	—	66.7	33.3	—	33.3
Germany	—	—	—	—	—	—	—	—	—	—	—	—	—	—	—	—	—	—	—	—	—
Hungary	100.0	—	100.0	—	—	—	—	—	—	—	—	—	—	—	—	100.0	—	100.0	—	—	—
Roumania	—	—	—	—	—	—	—	—	—	—	—	—	—	—	—	—	—	—	—	—	—
All foreign-born	100.0	100.0	100.0	—	—	—	4.3	—	3.7	—	—	—	—	—	—	91.3	100.0	92.6	4.3	—	3.7

TABLE 112—Native Jewish first admissions with psychoses with cerebral arteriosclerosis to all hospitals for mental disease in New York State, 1939-1941, classified according to age.

Age (years)	Number			Per cent		
	Males	Females	Total	Males	Females	Total
40–44	—	3	3	—	5.9	3.0
45–49	1	1	2	2.0	2.0	2.0
50–54	8	4	12	16.0	7.8	11.9
55–59	7	5	12	14.0	9.8	11.9
60–64	8	5	13	16.0	9.8	12.9
65–69	13	11	24	26.0	21.6	23.8
70–74	5	11	16	10.0	21.6	15.8
75–79	5	9	14	10.0	17.6	13.9
80–84	2	1	3	4.0	2.0	3.0
85–89	1	1	2	2.0	2.0	2.0
Total	50	51	101	100.0	100.0	100.0

TABLE 113—Native non-Jewish white first admissions with psychoses with cerebral arteriosclerosis to all hospitals for mental disease in New York State, 1939-1941, classified according to age.

Age (years)	Number			Per cent		
	Males	Females	Total	Males	Females	Total
35–39	—	5	5	—	0.3	0.1
40–44	10	3	13	0.5	0.2	0.3
45–49	17	28	45	0.8	1.6	1.2
50–54	100	85	185	5.0	4.8	4.9
55–59	199	178	377	9.9	10.1	10.0
60–64	359	311	670	17.9	17.7	17.8
65–69	442	377	819	22.1	21.4	21.8
70–74	384	344	728	19.2	19.6	19.4
75–79	304	266	570	15.2	15.1	15.2
80–84	142	112	254	7.1	6.4	6.8
85–89	36	38	74	1.8	2.2	2.0
90–94	8	9	17	0.4	0.5	0.4
95–99	2	1	3	0.1	0.1	0.1
Total	2003	1757	3760	100.0	100.0	100.0

TABLE 114—Foreign-born Jewish first admissions with psychoses with cerebral arteriosclerosis to all hospitals for mental disease in New York State, 1939-1941, classified according to age.

Age (years)	Number			Per cent		
	Males	Females	Total	Males	Females	Total
40–44	—	1	1	—	0.2	0.1
45–49	6	12	18	1.3	2.1	1.7
50–54	30	29	59	6.5	5.1	5.7
55–59	69	87	156	14.9	15.2	15.1
60–64	86	119	205	18.6	20.8	19.8
65–69	104	134	238	22.5	23.4	23.0
70–74	86	88	174	18.6	15.4	16.8
75–79	52	69	121	11.3	12.1	11.7
80–84	17	21	38	3.7	3.7	3.7
85–89	8	8	16	1.7	1.4	1.6
90–94	3	3	6	0.7	0.5	0.6
95–99	1	—	1	0.2	—	0.1
Total	462	571	1033	100.0	100.0	100.0

TABLE 115—Foreign-born non-Jewish white first admissions with psychoses with cerebral arteriosclerosis to all hospitals for mental disease in New York State, 1939-1941, classified according to age.

Age (years)	Number			Per cent		
	Males	Females	Total	Males	Females	Total
35–39	—	1	1	—	0.1	*
40–44	4	2	6	0.2	0.2	0.2
45–49	19	15	34	1.1	1.3	1.2
50–54	118	56	174	7.0	4.9	6.1
55–59	206	105	311	12.2	9.2	11.0
60–64	316	225	541	18.7	19.7	19.1
65–69	369	241	610	21.8	21.1	21.5
70–74	298	214	512	17.6	18.7	18.1
75–79	215	177	392	12.7	15.4	13.8
80–84	97	74	171	5.7	6.4	6.0
85–89	38	29	67	2.2	2.5	2.4
90–94	10	5	15	0.6	0.4	0.5
95–99	1	—	1	0.1	—	*
Total	1691	1144	2835	100.0	100.0	100.0

*Less than 0.05.

TABLE 116—Native Jewish first admissions with psychoses with cerebral arteriosclerosis to all hospitals for mental disease in New York State, 1939–1941, classified according to nativity of parents and environment.

Nativity of parents	Total			Urban									Rural								
				Total			New York City			Other			Total			Farm			Non-farm		
	M	F	T	M	F	T	M	F	T	M	F	T	M	F	T	M	F	T	M	F	T
	Number																				
Russia	12	7	19	12	7	19	12	7	19	—	—	—	—	—	—	—	—	—	—	—	—
Poland	6	6	12	6	6	12	6	3	9	—	3	3	—	—	—	—	—	—	—	—	—
Austria	5	8	13	5	8	13	5	8	13	—	—	—	—	—	—	—	—	—	—	—	—
Germany	14	15	29	14	15	29	13	14	27	1	1	2	—	—	—	—	—	—	—	—	—
Hungary	—	1	1	—	1	1	—	1	1	—	—	—	—	—	—	—	—	—	—	—	—
Roumania	—	—	—	—	—	—	—	—	—	—	—	—	—	—	—	—	—	—	—	—	—
All native-born	50	51	101	47	51	98	45	47	92	2	4	6	3	—	3	—	—	—	3	—	3
	Per cent																				
Russia	100.0	100.0	100.0	100.0	100.0	100.0	100.0	100.0	100.0	—	—	—	—	—	—	—	—	—	—	—	—
Poland	100.0	100.0	100.0	100.0	100.0	100.0	100.0	50.0	75.0	—	50.0	25.0	—	—	—	—	—	—	—	—	—
Austria	100.0	100.0	100.0	100.0	100.0	100.0	100.0	100.0	100.0	—	—	—	—	—	—	—	—	—	—	—	—
Germany	100.0	100.0	100.0	100.0	100.0	100.0	92.9	93.3	93.1	7.1	6.7	6.9	—	—	—	—	—	—	—	—	—
Hungary	—	100.0	100.0	—	100.0	100.0	—	100.0	100.0	—	—	—	—	—	—	—	—	—	—	—	—
Roumania	—	—	—	—	—	—	—	—	—	—	—	—	—	—	—	—	—	—	—	—	—
All native-born	100.0	100.0	100.0	94.0	100.0	97.0	90.0	92.2	91.1	4.0	7.8	5.9	6.0	—	3.0	—	—	—	6.0	—	3.0

TABLE 117—Native Jewish first admissions with psychoses with cerebral arteriosclerosis to all hospitals for mental disease in New York State, 1939–1941, classified according to nativity of parents and use of alcohol.

Nativity of parents	Total			Abstinent			Moderate			Intemperate			Unascertained		
	M	F	T	M	F	T	M	F	T	M	F	T	M	F	T
							Number								
Russia	12	7	19	10	5	15	1	1	2	—	1	1	1	—	1
Poland	6	6	12	2	6	8	2	—	2	2	—	2	—	—	—
Austria	5	8	13	2	8	10	3	—	3	—	—	—	—	—	—
Germany	14	15	29	8	13	21	4	2	6	2	—	2	—	—	—
Hungary	—	1	1	—	1	1	—	—	—	—	—	—	—	—	—
Roumania	—	—	—	—	—	—	—	—	—	—	—	—	—	—	—
All native-born	50	51	101	30	45	75	14	5	19	4	1	5	2	—	2
							Per cent								
Russia	100.0	100.0	100.0	83.3	71.4	78.9	8.3	14.3	10.5	—	14.3	5.3	8.3	—	5.3
Poland	100.0	100.0	100.0	33.3	100.0	66.7	33.3	—	16.7	33.3	—	16.7	—	—	—
Austria	100.0	100.0	100.0	40.0	100.0	76.9	60.0	—	23.1	—	—	—	—	—	—
Germany	100.0	100.0	100.0	57.1	86.7	72.4	28.6	13.3	20.7	14.3	—	6.0	—	—	—
Hungary	—	100.0	100.0	—	100.0	100.0	—	—	—	—	—	—	—	—	—
Roumania	—	—	—	—	—	—	—	—	—	—	—	—	—	—	—
All native-born	100.0	100.0	100.0	60.0	88.2	74.3	28.0	9.8	18.8	8.0	2.0	5.0	4.0	—	2.0

TABLE 118—Foreign-born Jewish first admissions with psychoses with cerebral arteriosclerosis to all hospitals for mental disease in New York State, 1939–1941, classified according to nativity and environment.

Nativity of parents	Total			Urban									Rural								
				Total			New York City			Other			Total			Farm			Non-farm		
	M	F	T	M	F	T	M	F	T	M	F	T	M	F	T	M	F	T	M	F	T
Number																					
Russia	227	292	519	227	290	517	220	273	493	7	17	24	—	2	2	—	—	—	—	2	2
Poland	55	71	126	55	71	126	50	68	118	5	3	8	—	—	—	—	—	—	—	—	—
Austria	78	96	174	78	96	174	76	95	171	2	1	3	—	—	—	—	—	—	—	—	—
Germany	29	35	64	28	35	63	23	34	57	5	1	6	1	—	1	—	—	—	1	—	1
Hungary	28	29	57	27	29	56	27	29	56	—	—	—	1	—	1	1	—	1	—	—	—
Roumania	20	18	38	20	18	38	20	18	38	—	—	—	—	—	—	—	—	—	—	—	—
All foreign-born	462	571	1033	460	569	1029	439	542	981	21	27	48	2	2	4	1	—	1	1	2	3
Per cent																					
Russia	100.0	100.0	100.0	100.0	99.3	99.6	96.9	93.4	95.0	3.1	5.8	4.6	—	0.7	0.4	—	—	—	—	0.7	0.4
Poland	100.0	100.0	100.0	100.0	100.0	100.0	90.0	95.8	93.7	9.1	4.2	6.3	—	—	—	—	—	—	—	—	—
Austria	100.0	100.0	100.0	100.0	100.0	100.0	97.4	99.0	98.3	2.6	1.0	1.7	—	—	—	—	—	—	—	—	—
Germany	100.0	100.0	100.0	96.6	100.0	98.4	79.3	97.1	89.1	17.2	2.9	9.4	3.4	—	1.6	3.4	—	1.6	—	—	—
Hungary	100.0	100.0	100.0	96.4	100.0	98.2	96.4	100.0	98.2	—	—	—	3.6	—	1.8	3.6	—	1.8	—	—	—
Roumania	100.0	100.0	100.0	100.0	100.0	100.0	100.0	100.0	100.0	—	—	—	—	—	—	—	—	—	—	—	—
All foreign-born	100.0	100.0	100.0	99.6	99.6	99.6	95.0	94.9	95.0	4.5	4.7	4.6	0.4	0.4	0.4	0.2	—	0.1	0.2	0.4	0.3

TABLE 119—Foreign-born Jewish first admissions with psychoses with cerebral arteriosclerosis to all hospitals for mental disease in New York State, 1939–1941, classified according to nativity and use of alcohol.

Nativity of parents	Total			Abstinent			Moderate			Intemperate			Unascertained		
	M	F	T	M	F	T	M	F	T	M	F	T	M	F	T
							Number								
Russia	227	292	519	144	270	414	68	18	86	12	1	13	3	3	6
Poland	55	71	126	35	65	100	19	4	23	1	—	1	—	2	2
Austria	78	96	174	40	93	133	36	2	38	1	1	2	1	—	1
Germany	29	35	64	14	29	34	12	6	18	—	—	—	3	—	3
Hungary	28	29	57	19	25	44	8	4	12	1	—	1	—	—	—
Roumania	20	18	38	9	17	26	7	1	8	2	—	2	2	—	2
All boreign-born	462	571	1033	272	526	798	161	38	199	20	2	22	9	5	14
							Per cent								
Russia	100.0	100.0	100.0	63.4	92.4	79.8	30.0	6.2	16.6	5.3	0.3	2.5	1.3	1.0	1.2
Poland	100.0	100.0	100.0	63.6	91.5	79.4	34.5	5.6	18.3	1.8	—	0.8	—	2.8	1.6
Austria	100.0	100.0	100.0	51.3	96.9	76.4	46.2	2.1	21.8	1.3	1.0	1.2	1.3	—	0.6
Germany	100.0	100.0	100.0	48.3	82.9	67.2	41.4	17.1	28.1	—	—	—	10.3	—	4.7
Hungary	100.0	100.0	100.0	67.9	86.2	77.2	28.5	13.8	21.1	3.6	—	1.8	—	—	—
Roumania	100.0	100.0	100.0	45.0	94.4	68.4	35.0	5.6	21.1	10.0	—	5.3	10.0	—	5.3
All foreign-born	100.0	100.0	100.0	58.9	92.1	77.3	34.8	6.7	19.3	4.3	0.4	2.1	1.9	0.9	1.4

TABLE 120—Foreign-born Jewish first admissions with psychoses with cerebral arteriosclerosis to all hospitals for mental disease in New York State, 1939–1941, classified according to nativity and time in United States prior to admission.

Nativity	Total			Less than 1 year			1 to 4 years			5 to 9 years			10 to 14 years			15 years and over			Unascertained		
	M	F	T	M	F	T	M	F	T	M	F	T	M	F	T	M	F	T	M	F	T
	Number																				
Russia	227	292	519	—	1	1	—	3	3	3	—	3	6	7	13	213	280	493	5	1	6
Poland	55	71	126	—	1	1	—	—	—	—	2	2	2	2	4	52	66	118	1	—	1
Austria	78	96	174	—	1	1	—	2	2	1	1	2	1	1	2	75	91	166	1	—	1
Germany	29	35	64	—	1	1	4	2	6	1	—	1	—	—	—	24	31	55	—	1	1
Hungary	28	29	57	—	—	—	—	—	—	—	—	—	—	1	1	28	28	56	—	—	—
Roumania	20	18	38	—	—	—	—	—	—	—	—	—	—	—	—	20	18	38	—	—	—
All foreign-born	462	571	1033	—	5	5	4	8	12	5	3	8	10	13	23	434	540	974	9	2	11
	Per cent																				
Russia	100.0	100.0	100.0	—	0.3	0.2	—	1.0	0.6	1.3	—	0.6	2.6	2.4	2.5	93.8	95.9	95.0	2.2	0.3	1.2
Poland	100.0	100.0	100.0	—	1.4	0.8	—	—	—	—	2.8	1.6	3.6	2.8	3.2	94.5	93.0	93.7	1.8	—	0.8
Austria	100.0	100.0	100.0	—	1.0	0.6	—	2.1	1.1	1.3	1.0	1.1	1.3	1.0	1.1	96.2	94.8	95.4	1.3	—	0.6
Germany	100.0	100.0	100.0	—	2.9	1.6	13.8	5.7	9.4	3.4	—	1.6	—	—	—	82.8	88.6	85.9	—	2.9	1.6
Hungary	100.0	100.0	100.0	—	—	—	—	—	—	—	—	—	—	3.4	1.8	100.0	96.6	98.2	—	—	—
Roumania	100.0	100.0	100.0	—	—	—	—	—	—	—	—	—	—	—	—	100.0	100.0	100.0	—	—	—
All foreign-born	100.0	100.0	100.0	—	0.9	0.4	0.9	1.4	1.2	1.1	0.5	0.8	2.2	2.3	2.2	93.9	94.6	94.3	1.9	0.4	1.1

TABLE 121—Native Jewish first admissions with senile psychoses to all hospitals for mental disease in New York State, 1939-1941, classified according to age.

Age (years)	Number			Per cent		
	Males	Females	Total	Males	Females	Total
50–54	1	—	1	5.6	—	2.0
55–59	3	3	6	16.7	9.7	12.2
60–64	—	—	—	—	—	—
65–69	—	3	3	—	9.7	6.1
70–74	4	3	7	22.2	9.7	14.3
75–79	4	12	16	22.2	38.7	32.7
80–84	5	8	13	27.8	25.8	26.5
85–89	1	2	3	5.6	6.4	6.1
Total	18	31	49	100.0	100.0	100.0

TABLE 122—Native non-Jewish white first admissions with senile psychoses to all hospitals for mental disease in New York State, 1939-1941, classified according to age.

Age (years)	Number			Per cent		
	Males	Females	Total	Males	Females	Total
50–54	5	7	12	0.5	0.5	0.5
55–59	7	15	22	0.8	1.1	1.0
60–64	45	64	109	4.8	4.8	4.8
65–69	93	160	253	10.0	12.1	11.2
70–74	189	254	443	20.3	19.2	19.6
75–79	258	339	597	27.7	25.6	26.4
80–84	216	309	525	23.2	23.3	23.2
85–89	99	141	240	10.9	10.6	10.6
90–94	18	31	49	1.9	2.3	2.2
95–99	3	6	9	0.3	0.4	0.4
Total	933	1326	2259	100.0	100.0	100.0

TABLE 123—Foreign-born Jewish first admissions with senile psychoses to all hospitals for mental disease in New York State, 1939-1941, classified according to age.

Age (years)	Number			Per cent		
	Males	Females	Total	Males	Females	Total
40–44	1	—	1	0.6	—	0.2
45–49	—	3	3	—	0.9	0.6
50–54	—	—	—	—	—	—
55–59	2	1	3	1.3	0.3	0.6
60–64	6	27	33	3.8	8.3	6.9
65–69	16	46	62	10.3	14.2	12.9
70–74	34	81	115	21.8	24.9	23.9
75–79	47	71	118	30.1	21.8	24.5
80–84	31	59	90	19.9	18.2	18.7
85–89	16	21	37	10.3	6.4	7.7
90–94	2	13	15	1.3	4.0	3.1
95–99	—	3	3	—	0.9	0.6
100–104	1	—	1	0.6	—	0.2
Total	156	325	481	100.0	100.0	100.0

TABLE 124—Foreign-born non-Jewish white first admissions with senile psychoses to all hospitals for mental disease in New York State, 1939-1941, classified according to age.

Age (years)	Number			Per cent		
	Males	Females	Total	Males	Females	Total
50–54	2	8	10	0.3	0.8	0.6
55–59	5	9	14	0.7	0.9	0.8
60–64	32	45	77	4.2	4.5	4.4
65–69	61	110	171	7.9	11.1	9.7
70–74	177	199	376	23.0	20.1	21.4
75–79	207	227	434	26.9	22.9	24.7
80–84	190	220	410	24.7	22.2	23.3
85–89	69	131	200	9.0	13.2	11.4
90–94	23	38	61	3.0	3.8	3.4
95–99	2	3	5	0.3	0.3	0.3
100–104	1	1	2	0.1	0.1	0.1
Total	769	991	1760	100.0	100.0	100.0

TABLE 125—Native Jewish first admissions with senile psychoses to all hospitals for mental disease in New York State, 1939–1941, classified according to nativity of parents and environment.

Nativity of parents	Total			Urban									Rural								
				Total			New York City			Other			Total			Farm			Non-farm		
	M	F	T	M	F	T	M	F	T	M	F	T	M	F	T	M	F	T	M	F	T
	Number																				
Russia	—	2	2	—	2	2	—	1	1	—	1	1	—	—	—	—	—	—	—	—	—
Poland	1	—	1	1	—	1	1	—	1	—	—	—	—	—	—	—	—	—	—	—	—
Austria	—	—	—	—	—	—	—	—	—	—	—	—	—	—	—	—	—	—	—	—	—
Germany	11	17	28	11	16	27	10	14	24	1	2	3	—	1	1	—	—	—	—	1	1
Hungary	1	1	2	1	1	2	1	1	2	—	—	—	—	—	—	—	—	—	—	—	—
Roumania	—	—	—	—	—	—	—	—	—	—	—	—	—	—	—	—	—	—	—	—	—
All native-born	18	31	49	18	30	48	17	27	44	1	3	4	—	1	1	—	—	—	—	1	1
	Per cent																				
Russia	—	100.0	100.0	—	100.0	100.0	—	50.0	50.0	—	50.0	50.0	—	—	—	—	—	—	—	—	—
Poland	100.0	—	100.0	100.0	—	100.0	100.0	—	100.0	—	—	—	—	—	—	—	—	—	—	—	—
Austria	—	—	—	—	—	—	—	—	—	—	—	—	—	—	—	—	—	—	—	—	—
Germany	100.0	100.0	100.0	100.0	94.1	96.4	90.9	82.4	85.7	9.1	11.8	10.7	—	5.9	3.6	—	—	—	—	5.9	3.6
Hungary	100.0	100.0	100.0	100.0	100.0	100.0	100.0	100.0	100.0	—	—	—	—	—	—	—	—	—	—	—	—
Roumania	—	—	—	—	—	—	—	—	—	—	—	—	—	—	—	—	—	—	—	—	—
All native-born	100.0	100.0	100.0	100.0	96.3	98.0	94.4	87.1	89.8	5.6	9.7	8.2	—	3.2	2.0	—	—	—	—	3.2	2.0

TABLE 126—Native Jewish first admissions with senile psychoses to all hospitals for mental disease in New York State, 1939–1941, classified according to nativity of parents and use of alcohol.

Nativity of parents	Total			Abstinent			Moderate			Intemperate			Unascertained		
	M	F	T	M	F	T	M	F	T	M	F	T	M	F	T
							Number								
Russia	—	2	2	—	2	2	—	—	—	—	—	—	—	—	—
Poland	1	—	1	1	—	1	—	—	—	—	—	—	—	—	—
Austria	—	—	—	—	—	—	—	—	—	—	—	—	—	—	—
Germany	11	17	28	6	15	21	5	2	7	—	—	—	—	—	—
Hungary	1	1	2	1	1	2	—	—	—	—	—	—	—	—	—
Roumania	—	—	—	—	—	—	—	—	—	—	—	—	—	—	—
All native-born	18	31	49	8	28	36	10	3	13	—	—	—	—	—	—
							Per cent								
Russia	—	100.0	100.0	—	100.0	100.0	—	—	—	—	—	—	—	—	—
Poland	100.0	—	100.0	100.0	—	100.0	—	—	—	—	—	—	—	—	—
Austria	—	—	—	—	—	—	—	—	—	—	—	—	—	—	—
Germany	100.0	100.0	100.0	54.5	88.2	75.0	45.4	11.8	25.0	—	—	—	—	—	—
Hungary	100.0	100.0	100.0	100.0	100.0	100.0	—	—	—	—	—	—	—	—	—
Roumania	—	—	—	—	—	—	—	—	—	—	—	—	—	—	—
All native born	100.0	100.0	100.0	44 4	90.3	73.4	55.6	9.7	26.5	—	—	—	—	—	—

TABLE 127—Foreign-born Jewish first admissions with senile psychoses to all hospitals for mental disease in New York State, 1939–1941, classified according to nativity and environment.

Nativity of parents	Total			Urban									Rural								
				Total			New York City			Other			Total			Farm			Non-farm		
	M	F	T	M	F	T	M	F	T	M	F	T	M	F	T	M	F	T	M	F	T
									Number												
Russia	89	159	248	89	159	248	85	148	233	4	11	15	—	—	—	—	—	—	—	—	—
Poland	18	39	57	18	39	57	15	39	54	3	—	3	—	—	—	—	—	—	—	—	—
Austria	20	51	71	20	51	71	17	51	68	3	—	3	—	—	—	—	—	—	—	—	—
Germany	11	32	43	10	32	42	9	30	39	1	2	3	1	—	1	—	—	—	1	—	1
Hungary	7	12	19	7	12	19	7	12	19	—	—	—	—	—	—	—	—	—	—	—	—
Roumania	5	14	19	5	14	19	5	14	19	—	—	—	—	—	—	—	—	—	—	—	—
All foreign-born	156	325	481	155	325	480	144	312	456	11	13	24	1	—	1	—	—	—	1	—	1
									Per cent												
Russia	100.0	100.0	100.0	100.0	100.0	100.0	95.5	93.1	94.0	4.5	6.9	6.0	—	—	—	—	—	—	—	—	—
Poland	100.0	100.0	100.0	100.0	100.0	100.0	83.3	100.0	94.7	16.7	—	5.3	—	—	—	—	—	—	—	—	—
Austria	100.0	100.0	100.0	100.0	100.0	100.0	85.0	100.0	95.8	15.0	—	4.2	—	—	—	—	—	—	—	—	—
Germany	100.0	100.0	100.0	90.9	100.0	97.7	81.8	93.8	90.7	9.1	6.3	7.0	9.1	—	2.3	—	—	—	9.1	—	2.3
Hungary	100.0	100.0	100.0	100.0	100.0	100.0	100.0	100.0	100.0	—	—	—	—	—	—	—	—	—	—	—	—
Roumania	100.0	100.0	100.0	100.0	100.0	100.0	100.0	100.0	100.0	—	—	—	—	—	—	—	—	—	—	—	—
All foreign-born	100.0	100.0	100.0	99.4	100.0	99.8	92.3	96.0	94.8	7.1	4.0	5.0	0.6	—	0.2	—	—	—	0.6	—	0.2

TABLE 128—Foreign-born Jewish first admissions with senile psychoses to all hospitals for mental disease in New York State, 1939–1941, classified according to nativity and use of alcohol.

Nativity of parents	Total			Abstinent			Moderate			Intemperate			Unascertained		
	M	F	T	M	F	T	M	F	T	M	F	T	M	F	T
Number															
Russia	89	159	248	53	153	206	25	4	29	5	—	5	6	2	8
Poland	18	39	57	10	37	47	8	2	10	—	—	—	—	—	—
Austria	20	51	71	13	48	61	5	3	8	1	—	1	1	—	1
Germany	11	32	43	5	25	30	5	4	9	—	3	3	1	—	1
Hungary	7	12	19	5	8	13	1	3	4	1	—	1	—	1	1
Roumania	5	14	19	2	13	15	2	1	3	—	—	—	1	—	1
All foreign-born	156	325	481	89	302	391	51	17	68	7	3	10	9	3	12
Percent															
Russia	100.0	100.0	100.0	59.6	96.2	83.1	28.1	2.5	11.7	5.6	—	2.0	6.7	1.3	3.2
Poland	100.0	100.0	100.0	55.6	94.9	82.4	44.4	5.1	17.5	—	—	—	—	—	—
Austria	100.0	100.0	100.0	65.0	94.1	85.9	25.0	5.9	11.3	5.0	—	1.4	5.0	—	1.4
Germany	100.0	100.0	100.0	45.4	78.1	69.8	45.4	12.5	20.9	—	9.4	7.0	9.1	—	2.3
Hungary	100.0	100.0	100.0	71.4	66.7	68.4	14.3	25.0	21.1	14.3	—	5.3	—	8.3	5.3
Roumania	100.0	100.0	100.0	40.0	92.9	78.9	40.0	7.1	15.8	—	—	—	20.0	—	5.3
All foreign-born	100.0	100.0	100.0	57.1	92.9	81.3	32.7	5.2	14.1	4.4	9.0	2.1	5.8	0.9	2.4

TABLE 129—Foreign-born Jewish first admissions with senile psychoses to all hospitals for mental disease in New York State, 1939–1941, classified according to nativity and time in United States prior to admission

Nativity	Total			Less than 1 year			1 to 4 years			5 to 9 years			10 to 14 years			15 years and over			Unascertained		
	M	F	T	M	F	T	M	F	T	M	F	T	M	F	T	M	F	T	M	F	T
	Number																				
Russia	89	159	248	1	—	1	3	—	3	—	2	2	1	4	5	82	153	235	2	—	2
Poland	18	39	57	—	—	—	—	—	—	—	—	—	—	4	4	18	35	53	—	—	—
Austria	20	51	71	—	—	—	—	—	—	—	—	—	—	1	1	19	50	69	1	—	1
Germany	11	32	43	—	1	1	1	3	4	—	1	1	—	1	1	10	25	35	—	1	1
Hungary	7	12	19	—	1	1	1	—	1	1	—	1	—	1	1	5	7	12	—	3	3
Roumania	5	14	19	—	—	—	—	—	—	—	—	—	—	2	2	5	12	17	—	—	—
All foreign-born	156	325	481	1	2	3	5	3	8	2	6	8	1	14	15	144	296	440	3	4	7
	Per cent																				
Russia	100.0	100.0	100.0	1.1	—	0.4	3.4	—	1.2	—	1.3	0.8	1.1	2.5	2.0	92.1	96.2	94.8	2.2	—	0.8
Poland	100.0	100.0	100.0	—	—	—	—	—	—	—	—	—	—	10.3	7.0	100.0	89.7	93.0	—	—	—
Austria	100.0	100.0	100.0	—	—	—	—	—	—	—	—	—	—	2.0	1.4	95.0	98.0	97.2	5.0	—	1.4
Germany	100.0	100.0	100.0	—	3.1	2.3	9.1	9.4	9.3	—	3.1	2.3	—	3.1	2.3	90.9	78.1	81.4	—	3.1	2.3
Hungary	100.0	100.0	100.0	—	8.3	5.3	14.3	—	5.3	14.3	—	5.3	—	8.3	5.3	71.4	58.3	63.2	—	25.0	15.8
Roumania	100.0	100.0	100.0	—	—	—	—	—	—	—	—	—	—	14.3	10.5	100.0	85.7	89.4	—	—	—
All foreign-born	100.0	100.0	100.0	0.6	0.6	0.6	3.2	0.9	1.7	1.3	1.8	1.7	0.6	4.3	3.1	92.3	91.1	91.4	1.9	1.2	1.4

TABLE 130—Native Jewish first admissions with involutional psychoses to all hospitals for mental disease in New York State, 1939-1941, classified according to age.

Age (years)	Number			Per cent		
	Males	Females	Total	Males	Females	Total
35–39	—	1	1	—	1.1	0.8
40–44	4	14	18	13.3	14.9	14.5
45–49	6	33	39	20.0	35.1	31.4
50–54	7	22	29	23.3	23.4	23.4
55–59	9	17	26	30.0	18.1	21.0
60–64	4	6	10	13.3	6.4	8.1
65–69	—	1	1	—	1.1	0.8
Total	30	94	124	100.0	100.0	100.0

TABLE 131—Native non-Jewish white first admissions with involutional psychoses to all hospitals for mental disease in New York State, 1939-1941, classified according to age.

Age (years)	Number			Per cent		
	Males	Females	Total	Males	Females	Total
25–29	—	1	1	—	0.1	0.1
30–34	—	1	1	—	0.1	0.1
35–39	3	18	21	0.7	1.9	1.5
40–44	43	148	191	9.7	15.8	13.9
45–49	70	256	326	15.8	27.4	23.6
50–54	135	243	378	30.4	26.0	27.4
55–59	105	149	254	23.6	15.9	18.4
60–64	46	78	124	10.4	8.3	9.0
65–69	35	33	68	7.9	3.5	4.9
70–74	5	8	13	1.1	0.9	0.9
75–79	2	—	2	0.4	—	0.1
Total	444	935	1379	100.0	100.0	100.0

TABLE 132—Foreign-born Jewish first admissions with involutional psychoses to all hospitals for mental disease in New York State, 1939-1941, classified according to age.

Age (years)	Number			Per cent		
	Males	Females	Total	Males	Females	Total
35–39	1	4	5	0.8	1.1	1.0
40–44	8	47	55	6.3	12.7	11.1
45–49	30	95	125	23.4	25.7	25.2
50–54	49	119	168	38.3	32.3	33.8
55–59	28	68	96	21.9	18.4	19.3
60–64	8	34	42	6.3	9.2	8.4
65–69	1	2	3	0.8	0.5	0.6
70–74	3	—	3	2.3	—	0.6
Total	128	369	497	100.0	100.0	100.0

TABLE 133—Foreign-born non-Jewish white first admissions with involutional psychoses to all hospitals for mental disease in New York State, 1939-1941, classified according to age.

Age (years)	Number			Per cent		
	Males	Females	Total	Males	Females	Total
30–34	—	1	1	—	0.2	0.1
35–39	1	9	10	0.4	1.4	1.1
40–44	20	80	100	7.5	12.4	11.0
45–49	52	185	237	19.5	28.9	26.1
50–54	80	204	284	30.1	31.8	31.3
55–59	66	113	179	24.8	17.6	19.7
60–64	31	28	59	11.7	4.4	6.5
65–69	16	15	31	6.0	2.3	3.4
70–74	—	6	6	—	0.9	0.7
Total	266	641	907	100.0	100.0	100.0

TABLE 134—Native Jewish first admissions with involutional psychoses to all hospitals for mental disease in New York State, 1939–1941, classified according to nativity of parents and environment.

Nativity of parents	Total			Urban									Rural								
				Total			New York City			Other			Total			Farm			Non-farm		
	M	F	T	M	F	T	M	F	T	M	F	T	M	F	T	M	F	T	M	F	T
	Number																				
Russia	10	32	42	10	32	42	10	28	38	—	4	4	—	—	—	—	—	—	—	—	—
Poland	7	6	13	7	6	13	3	3	6	4	3	7	—	—	—	—	—	—	—	—	—
Austria	5	16	21	5	16	21	2	16	18	3	—	3	—	—	—	—	—	—	—	—	—
Germany	5	15	20	5	14	19	4	13	17	1	1	2	—	1	1	—	—	—	—	1	1
Hungary	1	4	5	1	4	5	1	4	5	—	—	—	—	—	—	—	—	—	—	—	—
Roumania	1	2	3	1	2	3	1	2	3	—	—	—	—	—	—	—	—	—	—	—	—
All native-born	30	94	124	30	93	123	22	82	104	8	11	19	—	1	1	—	—	—	—	1	1
	Per cent																				
Russia	100.0	100.0	100.0	100.0	100.0	100.0	100.0	87.5	90.4	—	12.5	9.5	—	—	—	—	—	—	—	—	—
Poland	100.0	100.0	100.0	100.0	100.0	100.0	42.9	50.0	46.2	57.1	50.0	53.8	—	—	—	—	—	—	—	—	—
Austria	100.0	100.0	100.0	100.0	100.0	100.0	40.0	100.0	85.7	60.0	—	14.3	—	—	—	—	—	—	—	—	—
Germany	100.0	100.0	100.0	100.0	93.3	95.0	80.0	86.7	85.0	20.0	6.7	10.0	—	6.7	5.0	—	—	—	—	6.7	5.0
Hungary	100.0	100.0	100.0	100.0	100.0	100.0	100.0	100.0	100.0	—	—	—	—	—	—	—	—	—	—	—	—
Roumania	100.0	100.0	100.0	100.0	100.0	100.0	100.0	100.0	100.0	—	—	—	—	—	—	—	—	—	—	—	—
All native-born	100.0	100.0	100.0	100.0	98.9	99.2	73.3	87.2	83.9	26.7	11.7	15.3	—	1.1	0.8	—	—	—	—	1.1	0.8

TABLE 135—Native Jewish first admissions with involutional psychoses to all hospitals for mental disease in New York State, 1939–1941, classified according to nativity of parents and use of alcohol.

Nativity of parents	Total			Abstinent			Moderate			Intemperate			Unascertained		
	M	F	T	M	F	T	M	F	T	M	F	T	M	F	T
	Number														
Russia	10	32	42	5	31	36	2	1	3	3	—	3	—	—	—
Poland	7	6	13	7	6	13	—	—	—	—	—	—	—	—	—
Austria	5	16	21	1	12	13	4	3	7	—	—	—	—	1	1
Germany	5	15	20	4	12	16	1	3	4	—	—	—	—	—	—
Hungary	1	4	5	1	3	4	—	1	1	—	—	—	—	—	—
Roumania	1	2	3	1	2	3	—	—	—	—	—	—	—	—	—
All native-born	30	94	124	19	80	99	8	12	20	3	—	3	—	2	2
	Per cent														
Russia	100.0	100.0	100.0	50.0	96.9	85.7	20.0	3.1	7.1	3.0	—	7.1	—	—	—
Poland	100.0	100.0	100.0	100.0	100.0	100.0	—	—	—	—	—	—	—	—	—
Austria	100.0	100.0	100.0	20.0	75.0	61.9	80.0	18.8	33.3	—	—	—	—	6.3	4.8
Germany	100.0	100.0	100.0	80.0	80.0	80.0	20.0	20.0	20.0	—	—	—	—	—	—
Hungary	100.0	100.0	100.0	100.0	75.0	80.0	—	25.0	20.0	—	—	—	—	—	—
Roumania	100.0	100.0	100.0	100.0	100.0	100.0	—	—	—	—	—	—	—	—	—
All native-born	100.0	100.0	100.0	63.3	85.1	79.8	26.7	12.8	16.1	10.0	—	2.4	—	2.1	1.6

TABLE 136—Foreign-born Jewish first admissions with involutional psychoses to all hospitals for mental disease in New York State, 1939–1941, classified according to nativity and environment.

Nativity of parents	Total			Urban									Rural								
				Total			New York City			Other			Total			Farm			Non-farm		
	M	F	T	M	F	T	M	F	T	M	F	T	M	F	T	M	F	T	M	F	T
Number																					
Russia	60	185	245	59	185	244	57	174	231	2	11	13	1	—	1	—	—	—	1	—	1
Poland	27	66	93	27	66	93	26	59	85	1	7	8	—	—	—	—	—	—	—	—	—
Austria	19	54	73	19	54	73	18	54	72	1	—	1	—	—	—	—	—	—	—	—	—
Germany	3	5	8	3	5	8	3	4	7	—	1	1	—	—	—	—	—	—	—	—	—
Hungary	6	24	30	3	23	26	3	23	26	—	—	—	3	1	4	—	—	—	3	1	4
Roumania	5	12	17	5	12	17	5	11	16	—	1	1	—	—	—	—	—	—	—	—	—
All foreign-born	128	369	497	124	368	492	118	347	465	6	21	27	4	1	5	—	—	—	4	1	5
Per cent																					
Russia	100.0	100.0	100.0	98.3	100.0	99.6	95.0	94.1	94.3	3.3	5.9	5.3	1.7	—	0.4	—	—	—	1.7	—	0.4
Poland	100.0	100.0	100.0	100.0	100.0	100.0	96.3	89.4	91.4	3.7	10.6	8.6	—	—	—	—	—	—	—	—	—
Austria	100.0	100.0	100.0	100.0	100.0	100.0	94.7	100.0	98.6	5.3	—	1.4	—	—	—	—	—	—	—	—	—
Germany	100.0	100.0	100.0	100.0	100.0	100.0	100.0	80.0	87.5	—	20.0	12.5	—	—	—	—	—	—	—	—	—
Hungary	100.0	100.0	100.0	50.0	95.8	86.7	50.0	95.8	86.7	—	—	—	50.0	4.2	13.3	—	—	—	50.0	4.2	13.3
Roumania	100.0	100.0	100.0	100.0	100.0	100.0	100.0	91.7	94.1	—	8.3	5.9	—	—	—	—	—	—	—	—	—
All foreign-born	100.0	100.0	100.0	96.9	99.7	99.0	92.2	94.0	93.6	4.7	5.7	5.4	3.1	0.3	1.0	—	—	—	3.1	0.3	1.0

TABLE 137—Foreign-born Jewish first admissions with involutional psychoses to all hosptials for mental disease in New York State, 1939–1941, classified according to nativity and use of alcohol.

Nativity of parents	Total			Abstinent			Moderate			Intemperate			Unascertained		
	M	F	T	M	F	T	M	F	T	M	F	T	M	F	T
							Number								
Russia	60	185	245	39	167	206	15	12	27	3	—	3	3	9	6
Poland	27	66	93	21	56	77	6	10	16	—	—	—	—	—	—
Austria	19	54	73	12	45	57	5	5	10	2	—	2	—	4	4
Germany	3	5	8	3	5	8	—	—	—	—	—	—	—	—	—
Hungary	6	24	30	5	18	23	1	5	6	—	—	—	—	1	1
Roumania	5	12	17	5	10	15	—	2	2	—	—	—	—	—	—
All foreign-born	128	369	497	89	323	412	31	34	65	5	—	5	3	12	15
							Per cent								
Russia	100.0	100.0	100.0	65.0	90.3	64.1	25.0	6.4	11.0	5.0	—	1.2	5.0	3.2	3.7
Poland	100.0	100.0	100.0	77.8	84.8	82.8	22.2	15.2	17.2	—	—	—	—	—	—
Austria	100.0	100.0	100.0	63.2	83.3	78.1	26.3	9.3	13.7	10.5	—	2.7	—	7.4	5.4
Germany	100.0	100.0	100.0	100.0	100.0	100.0	—	—	—	—	—	—	—	—	—
Hungary	100.0	100.0	100.0	83.3	75.0	76.4	16.7	20.8	19.9	—	—	—	—	4.2	3.3
Roumania	100.0	100.0	100.0	100.0	83.3	88.2	—	16.7	11.8	—	—	—	—	—	—
All foreign-born	100.0	100.0	100.0	69.5	87.5	80.9	24.2	9.2	13.1	3.9	—	1.0	2.3	3.3	3.0

TABLE 138—Foreign-born Jewish first admissions with involutional psychoses to all hospitals for mental disease in New York State, 1939–1941, classified according to nativity and time in United States prior to admission.

Nativity	Total			Less than 1 year			1 to 4 years			5 to 9 years			10 to 14 years			15 years and over			Unascertained		
	M	F	T	M	F	T	M	F	T	M	F	T	M	F	T	M	F	T	M	F	T
Number																					
Russia	60	185	245	2	—	2	—	—	—	—	2	2	2	3	5	56	174	230	—	6	6
Poland	27	66	93	—	—	—	—	—	—	—	2	2	2	9	11	25	55	80	—	—	—
Austria	19	54	73	4	—	4	—	1	1	—	1	1	—	—	—	15	52	67	—	—	—
Germany	3	5	8	—	—	—	2	—	2	—	—	—	—	—	—	1	5	6	—	—	—
Hungary	6	24	30	—	—	—	—	1	1	—	—	—	—	1	1	6	22	28	—	—	—
Roumania	5	12	17	—	—	—	—	—	—	—	—	—	—	—	—	5	12	17	—	—	—
All foreign-born	128	369	497	6	—	6	2	3	5	—	6	6	4	15	19	116	339	455	—	6	6
Per cent																					
Russia	100.0	100.0	100.0	3.3	—	0.8	—	—	—	—	1.1	0.8	3.3	1.6	2.0	93.3	94.1	93.9	—	3.2	2.4
Poland	100.0	100.0	100.0	—	—	—	—	—	—	—	3.0	2.2	7.4	13.6	11.8	92.6	83.3	86.0	—	—	—
Austria	100.0	100.0	100.0	21.0	—	5.4	—	1.9	1.4	—	1.9	1.4	—	—	—	79.0	96.3	91.8	—	—	—
Germany	100.0	100.0	100.0	—	—	—	66.7	—	25.0	—	—	—	—	—	—	33.3	100.0	75.0	—	—	—
Hungary	100.0	100.0	100.0	—	—	—	—	4.2	3.3	—	—	—	—	4.2	3.3	100.0	91.7	93.3	—	—	—
Roumania	100.0	100.0	100.0	—	—	—	—	—	—	—	—	—	—	—	—	100.0	100.0	100.0	—	—	—
All foreign-born	100.0	100.0	100.0	4.7	—	1.2	1.6	0.8	1.0	—	1.6	1.2	3.1	4.1	3.8	90.6	91.9	91.5	—	1.6	1.2

TABLE 139—Native Jewish first admissions with manic-depressive psychoses to all hospitals for mental disease in New York State, 1939-1941, classified according to age.

Age (years)	Number			Per cent		
	Males	Females	Total	Males	Females	Total
10–14	—	1	1	—	0.3	0.2
15–19	17	25	42	12.3	7.0	8.4
20–24	16	66	82	11.6	18.5	16.6
25–29	26	62	88	18.8	17.4	17.8
30–34	27	56	83	19.6	15.7	16.8
35–39	19	68	87	13.8	19.0	17.6
40–44	20	25	45	14.4	7.0	9.1
45–49	8	29	37	5.8	8.1	7.4
50–54	5	8	13	3.6	2.2	2.6
55–59	—	4	4	—	1.1	0.8
60–64	—	5	5	—	1.4	1.0
65–69	—	3	3	—	0.8	0.6
70–74	—	5	5	—	1.4	1.0
Total	138	357	495	100.0	100.0	100.0

TABLE 140—Native non-Jewish white first admissions with manic-depressive psychoses to all hospitals for mental disease in New York State, 1939-1941, classified according to age.

Age (years)	Number			Per cent		
	Males	Females	Total	Males	Females	Total
10–14	2	2	4	0.3	0.2	0.2
15–19	25	52	77	3.8	4.0	3.9
20–24	76	158	234	11.7	12.1	11.9
25–29	74	184	258	11.3	14.1	13.2
30–34	64	233	297	9.8	17.8	15.2
35–39	82	195	277	12.6	14.9	14.1
40–44	78	138	216	12.0	10.6	11.0
45–49	100	96	196	15.3	7.3	10.0
50–54	63	105	168	9.7	8.0	8.6
55–59	44	61	105	6.7	4.7	5.4
60–64	28	44	72	4.3	3.4	3.7
65–69	11	28	39	1.7	2.1	2.0
70–74	4	11	15	0.6	0.8	0.8
75–79	—	—	—	—	—	—
80–84	1	1	2	0.2	0.1	0.1
Total	652	1308	1960	100.0	100.0	100.0

TABLE 141—Foreign-born Jewish first admissions with manic-depressive psychoses to all hospitals for mental disease in New York State, 1939-1941, classified according to age.

Age (years)	Number			Per cent		
	Males	Females	Total	Males	Females	Total
15–19	—	2	2	—	0.8	0.6
20–24	—	2	2	—	0.8	0.6
25–29	3	22	25	3.0	8.4	7.0
30–34	8	30	38	8.0	11.6	10.6
35–39	6	48	54	6.0	18.5	15.0
40–44	25	49	74	25.0	18.9	20.6
45–49	14	48	62	10.4	18.5	17.3
50–54	22	26	48	22.0	10.0	13.4
55–59	9	17	26	9.0	6.6	7.2
60–64	7	10	17	7.0	3.9	4.7
65–69	3	3	6	3.0	1.2	1.7
70–74	2	1	3	2.0	0.4	0.8
75–79	1	1	2	1.0	0.4	0.6
Total	100	259	359	100.0	100.0	100.0

TABLE 142—Foreign-born non-Jewish white first admissions with manic-depressive psychoses to all hospitals for mental disease in New York State, 1939-1941, classified according to age.

Age (years)	Number			Per cent		
	Males	Females	Total	Males	Females	Total
15–19	4	6	10	2.0	1.6	1.8
20–24	13	20	33	6.6	5.4	5.8
25–29	8	25	33	4.0	6.7	5.8
30–34	18	57	75	9.1	15.3	13.1
35–39	16	91	107	8.1	24.4	18.7
40–44	27	54	81	13.6	14.4	14.2
45–49	35	46	81	17.7	12.3	14.2
50–54	36	28	64	18.2	7.5	11.2
55–59	23	19	42	11.6	5.1	7.4
60–64	16	14	30	8.1	3.8	5.3
65–69	1	10	11	0.5	2.7	1.9
70–74	—	3	3	—	0.8	0.5
75–79	1	—	1	0.5	—	0.2
Total	198	373	571	100.0	100.0	100.0

TABLE 143—Native Jewish first admissions with manic-depressive psychoses to all hospitals for mental disease in New York State, 1939–1941, classified according to nativity of parents and environment.

Nativity of parents	Total			Urban									Rural								
				Total			New York City			Other			Total			Farm			Non-farm		
	M	F	T	M	F	T	M	F	T	M	F	T	M	F	T	M	F	T	M	F	T
	Number																				
Russia	66	161	227	66	159	225	59	138	197	7	21	28	—	2	2	—	—	—	—	2	2
Poland	7	38	45	7	38	45	7	31	38	—	7	7	—	—	—	—	—	—	—	—	—
Austria	19	59	78	19	59	78	19	58	77	—	1	1	—	—	—	—	—	—	—	—	—
Germany	3	19	22	3	19	22	3	16	19	—	3	3	—	—	—	—	—	—	—	—	—
Hungary	3	19	22	3	19	22	3	17	20	—	2	2	—	—	—	—	—	—	—	—	—
Roumania	8	21	29	8	21	29	5	18	23	3	3	6	—	—	—	—	—	—	—	—	—
All native-born	138	357	495	138	355	493	111	313	424	27	42	69	—	2	2	—	—	—	—	2	2
	Per cent																				
Russia	100.0	100.0	100.0	100.0	98.8	99.1	89.4	85.7	86.8	10.6	13.0	12.3	—	1.2	0.9	—	—	—	—	1.2	0.9
Poland	100.0	100.0	100.0	100.0	100.0	100.0	100.0	81.6	84.4	—	18.4	15.6	—	—	—	—	—	—	—	—	—
Austria	100.0	100.0	100.0	100.0	100.0	100.0	100.0	98.3	98.7	—	1.7	1.3	—	—	—	—	—	—	—	—	—
Germany	100.0	100.0	100.0	100.0	100.0	100.0	100.0	84.2	86.4	—	15.8	13.6	—	—	—	—	—	—	—	—	—
Hungary	100.0	100.0	100.0	100.0	100.0	100.0	100.0	89.4	90.9	—	10.5	9.1	—	—	—	—	—	—	—	—	—
Roumania	100.0	100.0	100.0	100.0	100.0	100.0	62.5	85.7	79.3	37.5	14.3	20.7	—	—	—	—	—	—	—	—	—
All native-born	100.0	100.0	100.0	100.0	99.4	99.6	80.4	87.7	85.7	19.6	11.8	13.9	—	0.6	0.4	—	—	—	—	0.6	0.4

TABLE 144—Native Jewish first admissions with manic-depressive psychoses to all hospitals for mental disease in New York State, 1939–1941, classified according to nativity of parents and use of alcohol.

Nativity of parents	Total			Abstinent			Moderate			Intemperate			Unascertained		
	M	F	T	M	F	T	M	F	T	M	F	T	M	F	T
Number															
Russia	66	161	227	27	121	148	25	30	55	4	—	4	10	10	20
Poland	7	38	45	4	29	33	1	6	7	1	—	1	1	3	4
Austria	19	59	78	8	52	60	11	4	15	—	—	—	—	3	3
Germany	3	19	22	3	14	17	—	5	5	—	—	—	—	—	—
Hungary	3	19	22	2	17	19	1	2	3	—	—	—	—	—	—
Roumania	8	21	29	8	9	17	—	9	9	—	—	—	—	3	3
All native-born	138	357	495	72	267	339	47	70	117	8	1	9	11	19	30
Percent															
Russia	100.0	100.0	100.0	40.9	75.2	65.2	37.9	18.6	24.3	6.1	—	1.8	15.2	6.2	8.8
Poland	100.0	100.0	100.0	57.1	76.3	73.3	14.3	15.8	15.6	14.3	—	2.2	14.3	7.9	8.9
Austria	100.0	100.0	100.0	42.1	88.1	76.9	57.9	6.8	19.2	—	—	—	—	5.1	3.8
Germany	100.0	100.0	100.0	100.0	73.7	77.3	—	26.3	22.7	—	—	—	—	—	—
Hungary	100.0	100.0	100.0	66.7	89.4	86.4	33.3	10.5	13.6	—	—	—	—	—	—
Roumania	100.0	100.0	100.0	100.0	42.9	58.6	—	42.9	31.0	—	—	—	—	14.3	10.3
All native-born	100.0	100.0	100.0	52.2	74.8	68.4	34.1	19.6	23.6	5.8	0.3	1.8	8.0	5.3	6.1

TABLE 145—Foreign-born Jewish first admissions with manic-depressive psychoses to all hospitals for mental disease in New York State, 1939–1941, classified according to nativity and environment.

Nativity of parents	Total			Urban									Rural								
				Total			New York City			Other			Total			Farm			Non-farm		
	M	F	T	M	F	T	M	F	T	M	F	T	M	F	T	M	F	T	M	F	T
	Number																				
Russia	49	103	152	49	103	152	41	93	134	8	10	18	—	—	—	—	—	—	—	—	—
Poland	13	44	57	13	44	57	12	36	48	1	8	9	—	—	—	—	—	—	—	—	—
Austria	15	43	58	15	43	58	15	42	57	—	1	1	—	—	—	—	—	—	—	—	—
Germany	6	27	33	6	27	33	3	27	30	3	—	3	—	—	—	—	—	—	—	—	—
Hungary	2	10	12	2	10	12	2	10	12	—	—	—	—	—	—	—	—	—	—	—	—
Roumania	2	8	10	2	8	10	2	7	9	—	1	1	—	—	—	—	—	—	—	—	—
All foreign-born	100	259	359	100	259	359	88	238	326	12	21	33	—	—	—	—	—	—	—	—	—
	Per cent																				
Russia	100.0	100.0	100.0	100.0	100.0	100.0	83.7	90.3	88.2	16.3	9.7	11.8	—	—	—	—	—	—	—	—	—
Poland	100.0	100.0	100.0	100.0	100.0	100.0	92.3	81.8	84.2	7.7	18.2	15.8	—	—	—	—	—	—	—	—	—
Austria	100.0	100.0	100.0	100.0	100.0	100.0	100.0	97.7	98.3	—	2.3	1.7	—	—	—	—	—	—	—	—	—
Germany	100.0	100.0	100.0	100.0	100.0	100.0	50.0	100.0	90.0	50.0	—	9.1	—	—	—	—	—	—	—	—	—
Hungary	100.0	100.0	100.0	100.0	100.0	100.0	100.0	100.0	100.0	—	—	—	—	—	—	—	—	—	—	—	—
Roumania	100.0	100.0	100.0	100.0	100.0	100.0	100.0	87.5	90.0	—	12.5	10.0	—	—	—	—	—	—	—	—	—
All foreign-born	100.0	100.0	100.0	100.0	100.0	100.0	88.0	91.9	90.8	12.0	8.1	9.2	—	—	—	—	—	—	—	—	—

TABLE 146—Foreign-born Jewish first admissions with manic-depressive psychoses to all hospitals for mental disease in New York State, 1939–1941, classified according to nativity and use of alcohol.

Nativity of parents	Total			Abstinent			Moderate			Intemperate			Unascertained		
	M	F	T	M	F	T	M	F	T	M	F	T	M	F	T
								Number							
Russia	49	103	152	22	92	114	17	7	24	1	—	1	9	4	13
Poland	13	44	57	6	31	37	7	10	17	—	—	—	—	3	3
Austria	15	43	58	10	34	44	5	—	5	—	—	—	—	9	9
Germany	6	27	33	3	24	27	3	3	6	—	—	—	—	—	—
Hungary	2	10	12	—	5	5	2	5	7	—	—	—	—	—	—
Roumania	2	8	10	1	8	9	1	—	1	—	—	—	—	—	—
All foreign-born	100	259	359	50	214	264	40	29	69	1	—	1	9	16	25
								Per cent							
Russia	100.0	100.0	100.0	44.9	89.3	75.0	34.7	6.8	15.8	2.0	—	0.7	18.4	3.9	8.6
Poland	100.0	100.0	100.0	46.2	70.4	64.9	53.8	22.7	29.8	—	—	—	—	6.8	5.3
Austria	100.0	100.0	100.0	66.7	79.1	75.9	33.3	—	8.6	—	—	—	—	20.9	15.5
Germany	100.0	100.0	100.0	50.0	88.9	81.8	50.0	11.1	18.2	—	—	—	—	—	—
Hungary	100.0	100.0	100.0	—	50.0	41.7	100.0	50.0	58.3	—	—	—	—	—	—
Roumania	100.0	100.0	100.0	50.0	100.0	90.0	50.0	—	10.0	—	—	—	—	—	—
All foreign-born	100.0	100.0	100.0	50.0	82.6	73.5	40.0	11.2	19.2	1.0	—	0.3	9.0	6.2	7.0

TABLE 147—Foreign-born Jewish first admissions with manic-depressive psychoses to all hospitals for mental disease in New York State, 1939–1941, classified according to nativity and time in United States prior to admission.

Nativity	Total			Less than 1 year			1 to 4 years			5 to 9 years			10 to 14 years			15 years and over			Unascertained		
	M	F	T	M	F	T	M	F	T	M	F	T	M	F	T	M	F	T	M	F	T
										Number											
Russia	49	103	152	2	2	4	—	—	—	—	—	—	1	—	1	46	97	143	—	4	4
Poland	13	44	57	—	1	1	1	—	1	—	—	—	1	2	3	11	38	49	—	3	3
Austria	15	43	58	—	10	10	3	—	3	1	—	1	—	1	1	11	32	43	—	—	—
Germany	6	27	33	2	9	11	1	13	14	1	4	5	—	—	—	2	1	3	—	—	—
Hungary	2	10	12	—	—	—	—	6	6	—	1	1	—	—	—	2	3	5	—	—	—
Roumania	2	8	10	—	4	4	—	—	—	—	—	—	1	1	2	1	3	4	—	—	—
All foreign-born	100	259	359	7	27	34	5	19	24	2	7	9	5	5	10	81	194	275	—	7	7
										Per cent											
Russia	100.0	100.0	100.0	4.1	1.9	2.6	—	—	—	—	—	—	2.0	—	0.7	93.9	94.2	94.1	—	3.9	2.6
Poland	100.0	100.0	100.0	—	2.3	1.8	7.7	—	1.8	—	—	—	7.7	4.5	5.3	84.6	86.4	86.0	—	6.8	5.3
Austria	100.0	100.0	100.0	—	23.3	17.2	20.0	—	5.2	6.7	—	1.7	—	2.3	1.7	73.3	74.4	74.1	—	—	—
Germany	100.0	100.0	100.0	33.3	33.3	33.3	16.7	48.1	42.4	16.7	14.8	15.2	—	—	—	33.3	3.7	9.1	—	—	—
Hungary	100.0	100.0	100.0	—	—	—	—	60.0	50.0	—	10.0	8.3	—	—	—	100.0	30.0	41.7	—	—	—
Roumania	100.0	100.0	100.0	—	50.0	40.0	—	—	—	—	—	—	50.0	12.5	20.0	50.0	37.5	40.0	—	—	—
All foreign-born	100.0	100.0	100.0	7.0	10.4	9.4	5.0	7.3	6.7	2.0	2.7	2.5	5.0	1.9	2.8	81.0	74.9	76.6	—	2.7	1.9

TABLE 148—Native Jewish first admissions with dementia praecox to all hospitals for mental disease in New York State, 1939-1941, classified according to age.

Age (years)	Number			Per cent		
	Males	Females	Total	Males	Females	Total
10–14	17	5	22	2.3	0.7	1.5
15–19	174	129	303	23.4	18.2	20.9
20–24	220	174	493	29.5	24.6	27.1
25–29	145	172	317	19.4	24.3	21.8
30–34	94	109	203	12.6	15.4	14.0
35–39	56	70	126	7.5	9.9	8.7
40–44	25	31	56	3.4	4.4	3.9
45–49	9	13	22	1.2	1.8	1.5
50–54	1	2	3	0.1	0.3	0.2
55–59	1	2	3	0.1	0.3	0.2
60–64	—	1	1	—	0.1	0.1
65–69	3	—	3	0.4	—	0.2
Total	745	708	1453	100.0	100.0	100.0

TABLE 149—Native non-Jewish white first admissions with dementia praecox to all hospitals for mental disease in New York State, 1939-1941, classified according to age.

Age (years)	Number			Per cent		
	Males	Females	Total	Males	Females	Total
10–14	7	21	28	0.2	0.7	0.4
15–19	330	283	613	10.6	9.7	10.2
20–24	732	530	1262	23.4	18.2	20.9
25–29	687	576	1263	22.0	19.8	21.0
30–34	532	452	984	17.1	15.5	16.3
35–39	349	382	731	11.2	13.1	12.1
40–44	224	270	494	7.2	9.3	8.2
45–49	132	185	317	4.2	6.4	5.3
50–54	68	99	167	2.2	3.4	2.8
55–59	34	59	93	1.1	2.0	1.5
60–64	14	25	39	0.5	0.9	0.7
65–69	6	16	22	0.2	0.6	0.4
70–74	—	5	5	—	0.2	0.1
75–79	2	2	4	0.1	0.1	0.1
80–84	—	1	1	—	*	*
85–89	—	1	1	—	*	*
Total	3117	2907	6024	100.0	100.0	100.0

*Less than 0.05.

TABLE 150—Foreign-born Jewish first admissions with dementia praecox to all hospitals for mental disease in New York State, 1939-1941, classified according to age.

Age (years)	Number			Per cent		
	Males	Females	Total	Males	Females	Total
15–19	12	9	21	4.5	2.1	3.0
20–24	25	20	45	9.4	4.6	6.4
25–29	51	50	101	19.1	11.6	14.4
30–34	57	65	122	21.3	15.0	17.5
35–39	50	107	157	18.7	24.8	22.5
40–44	32	72	104	12.0	16.7	14.9
45–49	18	53	71	6.7	12.3	10.2
50–54	12	24	36	4.5	5.6	5.2
55–59	7	19	26	2.6	4.4	3.7
60–64	2	10	12	0.8	2.3	1.7
65–69	1	—	1	0.4	—	0.1
70–74	—	3	3	—	0.7	0.4
Total	267	432	699	100.0	100.0	100.0

TABLE 151—Foreign-born non-Jewish white first admissions with dementia praecox to all hospitals for mental disease in New York State, 1939-1941, classified according to age.

Age (years)	Number			Per cent		
	Males	Females	Total	Males	Females	Total
15–19	20	10	30	2.0	1.1	1.5
20–24	45	24	69	4.5	2.6	3.6
25–29	91	100	191	9.1	10.6	9.9
30–34	139	156	295	13.9	16.6	15.2
35–39	198	206	404	19.9	21.9	20.9
40–44	178	138	316	17.9	14.7	16.3
45–49	157	123	280	15.7	13.1	14.4
50–54	93	95	188	9.3	10.1	9.7
55–59	55	51	106	5.5	5.4	5.4
60–64	16	21	37	1.6	2.2	1.9
65–69	3	11	14	0.3	1.2	0.7
70–74	—	1	1	—	0.1	0.1
75–79	2	3	5	0.2	0.3	0.3
80–84	—	—	—	—	—	—
85–89	—	1	1	—	0.1	0.1
Total	997	940	1937	100.0	100.0	100.0

TABLE 152—Native Jewish first admissions with dementia praecox to all hospitals for mental disease in New York State, 1939–1941, classified according to nativity of parents and environment.

Nativity of parents	Total			Urban									Rural								
				Total			New York City			Other			Total			Farm			Non-farm		
	M	F	T	M	F	T	M	F	T	M	F	T	M	F	T	M	F	T	M	F	T
Number																					
Russia	371	388	759	366	385	751	341	366	707	25	19	44	5	3	8	1	—	1	4	3	7
Poland	84	74	158	84	74	158	70	68	138	14	6	20	—	—	—	—	—	—	—	—	—
Austria	111	95	206	111	95	206	110	87	197	1	8	9	—	—	—	—	—	—	—	—	—
Germany	25	9	34	25	9	34	24	9	33	1	—	1	—	—	—	—	—	—	—	—	—
Hungary	19	28	47	19	28	47	18	28	46	1	—	1	—	—	—	—	—	—	—	—	—
Roumania	32	34	66	32	34	66	30	31	61	2	3	5	—	—	—	—	—	—	—	—	—
All native-born	745	708	1453	739	705	1444	682	664	1346	57	41	98	6	3	9	1	—	1	5	3	8
Per cent																					
Russia	100.0	100.0	100.0	98.7	99.2	98.9	91.9	94.3	93.1	6.7	4.9	5.8	1.3	0.8	1.1	0.3	—	0.1	1.1	0.8	0.9
Poland	100.0	100.0	100.0	100.0	100.0	100.0	83.3	91.9	87.3	16.7	8.1	12.7	—	—	—	—	—	—	—	—	—
Austria	100.0	100.0	100.0	100.0	100.0	100.0	99.1	91.6	95.6	0.9	8.4	4.4	—	—	—	—	—	—	—	—	—
Germany	100.0	100.0	100.0	100.0	100.0	100.0	96.0	100.0	97.1	4.0	—	2.9	—	—	—	—	—	—	—	—	—
Hungary	100.0	100.0	100.0	100.0	100.0	100.0	94.7	100.0	97.9	5.3	—	2.1	—	—	—	—	—	—	—	—	—
Roumania	100.0	100.0	100.0	100.0	100.0	100.0	93.8	91.2	92.4	6.3	8.8	7.6	—	—	—	—	—	—	—	—	—
All native-born	100.0	100.0	100.0	99.2	99.6	99.4	91.5	93.8	92.6	7.7	5.8	6.7	0.8	0.4	0.6	0.1	—	0.1	0.7	0.4	0.6

TABLE 153—Native Jewish first admissions with dementia praecox to all hospitals for mental disease in New York State, 1939–1941, classified according to nativity of parents and use of alcohol.

Nativity of parents	Total			Abstinent			Moderate			Intemperate			Unascertained		
	M	F	T	M	F	T	M	F	T	M	F	T	M	F	T
Number															
Russia	371	388	759	296	333	629	62	34	96	3	—	3	10	21	31
Poland	84	74	158	61	66	127	22	5	27	1	—	1	—	3	3
Austria	111	95	206	77	70	147	30	22	52	1	—	1	3	3	6
Germany	25	9	34	16	7	23	8	2	10	—	—	—	1	—	1
Hungary	19	28	47	11	19	30	7	3	10	1	—	1	—	6	6
Roumania	32	34	66	24	30	54	8	2	10	—	1	1	—	1	1
All native-born	745	708	1453	546	590	1136	170	79	249	8	4	12	21	35	56
Per cent															
Russia	100.0	100.0	100.0	79.8	85.8	82.9	16.7	8.8	12.6	0.8	—	0.4	2.7	5.4	4.1
Poland	100.0	100.0	100.0	72.6	89.2	80.4	26.2	6.8	17.1	1.2	—	0.6	—	4.1	1.9
Austria	100.0	100.0	100.0	69.4	73.7	71.4	27.0	23.2	25.2	0.9	—	0.4	2.7	3.2	2.9
Germany	100.0	100.0	100.0	64.0	77.8	67.6	32.0	22.2	29.4	—	—	—	4.0	—	2.9
Hungary	100.0	100.0	100.0	57.9	67.9	63.8	36.8	10.7	21.3	5.3	—	2.1	—	21.4	12.8
Roumania	100.0	100.0	100.0	75.0	88.2	81.8	25.0	5.9	15.2	—	2.9	1.5	—	2.9	1.5
All native-born	100.0	100.0	100.0	73.3	83.3	78.2	22.8	11.2	17.1	1.1	0.6	0.8	2.8	4.9	3.9

TABLE 154—Foreign-born Jewish first admissions with dementia praecox to all hospitals for mental disease in New York State, 1939–1941, classified according to nativity and environment.

Nativity of parents	Total			Urban									Rural								
				Total			New York City			Other			Total			Farm			Non-farm		
	M	F	T	M	F	T	M	F	T	M	F	T	M	F	T	M	F	T	M	F	T
Number																					
Russia	99	190	289	98	190	288	87	181	268	11	9	20	1	—	1	1	—	1	—	—	—
Poland	83	91	174	82	91	173	79	83	162	3	8	11	1	—	1	—	—	—	1	—	1
Austria	33	45	78	33	45	78	33	43	76	—	2	2	—	—	—	—	—	—	—	—	—
Germany	13	23	36	13	23	36	13	23	36	—	—	—	—	—	—	—	—	—	—	—	—
Hungary	8	27	35	8	27	35	8	27	35	—	—	—	—	—	—	—	—	—	—	—	—
Roumania	6	18	24	6	18	24	3	17	20	3	1	4	—	—	—	—	—	—	—	—	—
All foreign-born	267	432	699	265	432	697	248	409	657	17	23	40	2	—	2	1	—	1	1	—	1
Per cent																					
Russia	100.0	100.0	100.0	99.0	100.0	99.7	87.9	95.3	92.7	11.1	4.7	6.9	1.0	—	0.3	1.0	—	0.3	—	—	—
Poland	100.0	100.0	100.0	98.8	100.0	99.4	95.2	91.2	93.1	3.6	8.8	6.3	1.2	—	0.6	—	—	—	1.2	—	0.6
Austria	100.0	100.0	100.0	100.0	100.0	100.0	100.0	95.6	97.4	—	4.4	2.6	—	—	—	—	—	—	—	—	—
Germany	100.0	100.0	100.0	100.0	100.0	100.0	100.0	100.0	100.0	—	—	—	—	—	—	—	—	—	—	—	—
Hungary	100.0	100.0	100.0	100.0	100.0	100.0	100.0	100.0	100.0	—	—	—	—	—	—	—	—	—	—	—	—
Roumania	100.0	100.0	100.0	100.0	100.0	100.0	50.0	94.4	83.3	50.0	5.6	16.7	—	—	—	—	—	—	—	—	—
All foreign-born	100.0	100.0	100.0	99.3	100.0	99.7	92.9	94.7	94.0	6.4	5.3	5.7	0.7	—	0.3	0.4	—	0.1	0.4	—	0.1

TABLE 155—Foreign-born Jewish first admissions with dementia praecox to all hospitals for mental disease in New York State, 1939–1941, classified according to nativity and use of alcohol.

Nativity of parents	Total			Abstinent			Moderate			Intemperate			Unascertained		
	M	F	T	M	F	T	M	F	T	M	F	T	M	F	T
							Number								
Russia	99	190	289	71	166	237	23	16	39	2	—	2	3	8	11
Poland	83	91	174	59	87	146	16	4	20	2	—	2	6	—	6
Austria	33	45	78	23	34	57	8	10	18	2	—	2	—	1	1
Germany	13	23	36	5	13	18	2	10	12	—	—	—	6	—	6
Hungary	8	27	35	7	23	30	1	3	4	—	—	—	—	1	1
Roumania	6	18	24	1	17	18	5	1	6	—	—	—	—	—	—
All foreign-born	267	432	699	184	373	557	62	45	107	6	1	7	15	13	28
							Per cent								
Russia	100.0	100.0	100.0	71.7	87.4	82.0	23.2	8.4	13.4	2.0	—	0.7	3.0	4.2	3.8
Poland	100.0	100.0	100.0	71.1	95.6	83.9	19.3	4.4	11.5	2.4	—	1.2	7.2	—	3.4
Austria	100.0	100.0	100.0	69.7	75.6	73.1	24.2	22.2	23.1	6.1	—	2.6	—	2.2	2.3
Germany	100.0	100.0	100.0	38.4	56.5	50.0	15.4	43.4	33.3	—	—	—	46.2	—	16.7
Hungary	100.0	100.0	100.0	87.5	85.2	85.7	12.5	11.1	11.4	—	—	—	—	3.7	2.9
Roumania	100.0	100.0	100.0	16.7	94.4	75.0	83.3	5.6	25.0	—	—	—	—	—	—
All foreign-born	100.0	100.0	100.0	68.9	86.3	79.7	23.2	10.4	15.3	2.2	0.2	1.0	5.6	3.0	4.0

TABLE 156—Foreign-born Jewish first admissions with dementia praecox to all hospitals for mental disease in New York State, 1939–1941, classified according to nativity and time in United States prior to admission.

Nativity	Total			Less than 1 year			1 to 4 years			5 to 9 years			10 to 14 years			15 years and over			Unascertained		
	M	F	T	M	F	T	M	F	T	M	F	T	M	F	T	M	F	T	M	F	T
										Number											
Russia	99	190	289	—	—	—	2	3	5	6	7	13	7	14	21	83	163	246	1	3	4
Poland	83	91	174	3	1	4	7	4	11	6	5	11	11	12	23	54	69	123	2	—	2
Austria	33	45	78	7	1	8	4	7	11	—	3	3	6	5	11	16	28	44	—	1	1
Germany	13	23	36	2	2	4	10	11	21	—	—	—	—	5	5	1	3	4	—	2	2
Hungary	8	27	35	—	3	3	—	—	—	—	1	1	—	2	2	8	21	29	—	—	—
Roumania	6	18	24	3	—	3	1	—	1	—	—	—	—	—	—	2	18	20	—	—	—
All foreign-born	267	432	699	18	8	26	26	28	54	13	17	30	32	42	74	175	330	505	3	7	10
										Per cent											
Russia	100.0	100.0	100.0	—	—	—	2.0	1.6	1.7	6.1	3.7	4.5	7.1	7.4	7.3	83.8	85.8	85.1	1.0	1.6	1.4
Poland	100.0	100.0	100.0	3.6	1.1	2.3	8.4	4.4	6.3	7.2	5.4	6.3	13.3	13.2	13.2	65.1	75.8	70.7	2.4	—	1.1
Austria	100.0	100.0	100.0	21.2	2.2	10.3	12.1	15.6	14.1	—	6.7	3.8	18.2	11.1	14.1	48.4	62.2	56.4	—	2.2	1.3
Germany	100.0	100.0	100.0	15.4	8.7	11.1	76.9	47.8	58.3	—	—	—	—	21.7	13.9	7.7	13.0	11.1	—	8.7	5.6
Hungary	100.0	100.0	100.0	—	11.1	8.6	—	—	—	—	3.7	2.9	—	7.4	5.7	100.0	77.8	82.9	—	—	—
Roumania	100.0	100.0	100.0	50.0	—	12.5	16.7	—	4.2	—	—	—	—	—	—	33.3	100.0	83.3	—	—	—
All foreign-born	100.0	100.0	100.0	6.7	1.9	3.7	9.7	6.4	7.7	4.9	3.9	4.3	12.0	9.7	10.6	65.5	76.4	72.2	1.1	1.6	1.4

TABLE 157—Native non-Jewish white first admissions with psychoneuroses to all hospitals for mental disease in New York State, 1939-1941, classified according to age.

Age (years)	Number			Per cent		
	Males	Females	Total	Males	Females	Total
5–9	—	1	1	—	0.1	0.1
10–14	5	5	10	0.8	0.6	0.7
15–19	16	31	47	2.7	3.8	3.3
20–24	48	68	116	8.0	8.3	8.2
25–29	57	145	202	9.5	7.7	14.3
30–34	87	114	201	14.5	13.9	14.2
35–39	79	108	187	13.2	13.2	13.2
40–44	85	90	175	14.2	11.0	12.4
45–49	78	61	139	13.0	7.5	9.8
50–54	66	68	134	11.0	8.3	9.4
55–59	41	51	92	6.8	6.2	6.4
60–64	23	40	63	3.8	4.9	4.4
65–69	13	25	38	2.2	3.1	2.7
70–74	—	10	10	—	1.2	0.7
75–79	1	—	1	0.2	—	0.1
80–84	—	1	1	—	0.1	0.1
Total	599	818	1417	100.0	100.0	100.0

TABLE 158—Native Jewish first admissions with psychoneuroses to all hospitals for mental disease in New York State, 1939-1941, classified according to age.

Age (years)	Number			Per cent		
	Males	Females	Total	Males	Females	Total
5–9	2	—	2	1.3	—	0.6
10–14	2	2	4	1.3	1.2	1.3
15–19	12	14	26	7.8	8.4	8.2
20–24	14	24	38	9.2	14.5	11.9
25–29	23	42	65	15.0	25.3	20.4
30–34	30	37	67	19.6	22.3	24.0
35–39	19	16	35	12.4	9.6	11.0
40–44	36	17	53	23.5	10.2	16.6
45–49	9	10	19	5.9	6.0	5.9
50–54	2	2	4	1.3	1.2	1.3
55–59	3	1	4	2.0	0.6	1.3
60–64	1	—	1	0.7	—	0.3
65–69	—	—	—	—	—	—
70–74	—	1	1	—	0.6	0.3
Total	153	166	319	100.0	100.0	100.0

TABLE 159—Foreign-born Jewish first admissions with psychoneuroses to all hospitals for mental disease in New York State, 1939-1941, classified according to age.

Age (years)	Number			Per cent		
	Males	Females	Total	Males	Females	Total
20–24	11	5	16	11.3	3.7	6.9
25–29	7	8	15	7.2	6.0	6.4
30–34	5	6	11	5.2	4.5	4.8
35–39	10	20	30	10.3	14.9	13.0
40–44	14	28	42	14.4	20.9	18.2
45–49	15	18	33	15.4	13.4	14.3
50–54	16	33	49	16.4	24.6	20.2
55–69	9	9	18	9.3	6.7	7.8
60–64	5	1	6	5.2	0.8	2.6
65–69	5	5	10	5.2	3.7	4.3
70–74	—	1	1	—	0.7	0.4
Total	97	134	231	100.0	100.0	100.0

TABLE 160—Foreign-born non-Jewish white first admissions with psychoneuroses to all hospitals for mental disease in New York State, 1939-1941, classified according to age.

Age (years)	Number			Per cent		
	Males	Females	Total	Males	Females	Total
10–14	—	1	1	—	0.6	0.3
15–19	1	1	2	0.6	0.6	0.6
20–24	3	3	6	1.9	1.7	1.8
25–29	6	10	16	3.8	5.8	4.8
30–34	11	28	39	7.0	16.2	11.8
35–39	24	31	55	15.2	17.9	16.6
40–44	20	29	49	12.7	16.8	14.8
45–49	29	16	45	18.4	9.2	13.6
50–54	21	21	42	13.3	12.1	12.7
55–59	26	15	41	16.4	8.7	12.4
60–64	15	12	27	9.4	6.9	8.2
65–69	2	4	6	1.3	2.3	1.8
70–74	—	1	1	—	0.6	0.3
75–79	—	—	—	—	—	—
80–84	—	1	1	—	0.6	0.3
Total	158	173	331	100.0	100.0	100.0

TABLE 161—Native Jewish first admissions with psychoneuroses to all hospitals for mental disease in New York State, 1939–1941, classified according to nativity of parents and environment.

Nativity of parents	Total			Urban									Rural								
				Total			New York City			Other			Total			Farm			Non-farm		
	M	F	T	M	F	T	M	F	T	M	F	T	M	F	T	M	F	T	M	F	T
	Number																				
Russia	71	87	158	71	87	158	69	78	147	2	9	11	—	—	—	—	—	—	—	—	—
Poland	13	15	28	12	15	27	10	12	22	2	3	5	1	—	1	—	—	—	1	—	1
Austria	23	31	54	23	31	54	18	31	49	5	—	5	—	—	—	—	—	—	—	—	—
Germany	5	11	16	5	11	16	5	8	13	—	3	3	—	—	—	—	—	—	—	—	—
Hungary	10	2	12	10	2	12	9	1	10	1	1	2	—	—	—	—	—	—	—	—	—
Roumania	6	3	9	6	3	9	3	3	6	3	—	3	—	—	—	—	—	—	—	—	—
All native-born	153	166	319	152	165	317	134	145	279	18	20	38	1	1	2	—	—	—	1	1	2
	Per cent																				
Russia	100.0	100.0	100.0	100.0	100.0	100.0	97.2	89.7	93.0	2.8	10.3	7.0	—	—	—	—	—	—	—	—	—
Poland	100.0	100.0	100.0	92.3	100.0	96.4	76.9	80.0	78.6	15.4	20.0	17.9	7.7	—	3.6	—	—	—	7.7	—	3.6
Austria	100.0	100.0	100.0	100.0	100.0	100.0	78.3	100.0	90.7	21.7	—	9.3	—	—	—	—	—	—	—	—	—
Germany	100.0	100.0	100.0	100.0	100.0	100.0	100.0	72.7	81.3	—	27.3	18.8	—	—	—	—	—	—	—	—	—
Hungary	100.0	100.0	100.0	100.0	100.0	100.0	90.0	50.0	83.3	10.0	50.0	16.7	—	—	—	—	—	—	—	—	—
Roumania	100.0	100.0	100.0	100.0	100.0	100.0	50.0	100.0	66.7	50.0	—	33.3	—	—	—	—	—	—	—	—	—
All native-born	100.0	100.0	100.0	99.3	99.4	99.4	87.6	87.3	87.5	11.8	12.0	11.9	0.7	0.6	0.6	—	—	—	0.7	0.5	0.6

TABLE 162—Native Jewish first admissions with psychoneuroses to all hospitals for mental disease in New York State, 1939–1941, classified according to nativity of parents and use of alcohol.

Nativity of parents	Total			Abstinent			Moderate			Intemperate			Unascertained		
	M	F	T	M	F	T	M	F	T	M	F	T	M	F	T
Number															
Russia	71	87	158	29	56	85	19	16	35	5	—	5	18	15	33
Poland	13	15	28	7	12	19	3	3	6	—	—	—	3	—	3
Austria	23	31	54	9	26	35	5	2	7	—	—	—	9	3	12
Germany	5	11	16	1	5	6	1	6	7	—	—	—	3	—	3
Hungary	10	2	12	3	2	5	7	—	7	—	—	—	—	—	—
Roumania	6	3	9	1	—	1	5	—	5	—	—	—	—	3	3
All native-born	153	166	319	66	108	174	45	34	79	9	—	9	33	24	57
Per cent															
Russia	100.0	100.0	100.0	40.8	64.4	53.8	26.7	18.4	22.2	7.0	—	3.2	25.4	17.2	20.9
Poland	100.0	100.0	100.0	53.8	80.0	67.9	23.1	20.0	21.4	—	—	—	23.1	—	10.7
Austria	100.0	100.0	100.0	39.1	83.9	64.8	21.7	6.4	13.0	—	—	—	39.1	9.7	22.2
Germany	100.0	100.0	100.0	20.0	45.5	37.5	20.0	54.5	43.8	—	—	—	60.0	—	18.8
Hungary	100.0	100.0	100.0	30.0	100.0	41.7	70.0	—	58.3	—	—	—	—	—	—
Roumania	100.0	100.0	100.0	16.7	—	11.1	83.3	—	55.6	—	—	—	—	100.0	33.3
All native-born	100.0	100.0	100.0	43.1	65.1	54.5	29.4	20.4	24.8	5.9	—	2.8	21.6	14.5	17.9

TABLE 163—Foreign-born Jewish first admissions with psychoneuroses to all hospitals for mental disease in New York State, 1939–1941, classified according to nativity and environment.

Nativity of parents	Total			Urban									Rural								
				Total			New York City			Other			Total			Farm			Non-farm		
	M	F	T	M	F	T	M	F	T	M	F	T	M	F	T	M	F	T	M	F	T
	Number																				
Russia	41	61	102	41	61	102	33	60	93	8	1	9	—	—	—	—	—	—	—	—	—
Poland	20	17	37	20	17	37	20	12	32	—	5	5	—	—	—	—	—	—	—	—	—
Austria	10	23	33	10	23	33	10	23	33	—	—	—	—	—	—	—	—	—	—	—	—
Germany	6	12	18	6	12	18	6	12	18	—	—	—	—	—	—	—	—	—	—	—	—
Hungary	4	7	11	4	7	11	4	7	11	—	—	—	—	—	—	—	—	—	—	—	—
Roumania	—	9	9	—	9	9	—	9	9	—	—	—	—	—	—	—	—	—	—	—	—
All foreign-born	97	134	231	97	134	231	85	127	212	12	7	19	—	—	—	—	—	—	—	—	—
	Per cent																				
Russia	100.0	100.0	100.0	100.0	100.0	100.0	80.5	98.4	91.2	19.5	1.6	8.8	—	—	—	—	—	—	—	—	—
Poland	100.0	100.0	100.0	100.0	100.0	100.0	100.0	70.6	86.5	—	29.4	13.5	—	—	—	—	—	—	—	—	—
Austria	100.0	100.0	100.0	100.0	100.0	100.0	100.0	100.0	100.0	—	—	—	—	—	—	—	—	—	—	—	—
Germany	100.0	100.0	100.0	100.0	100.0	100.0	100.0	100.0	100.0	—	—	—	—	—	—	—	—	—	—	—	—
Hungary	100.0	100.0	100.0	100.0	100.0	100.0	100.0	100.0	100.0	—	—	—	—	—	—	—	—	—	—	—	—
Roumania	—	100.0	100.0	—	100.0	100.0	—	100.0	100.0	—	—	—	—	—	—	—	—	—	—	—	—
All foreign-born	100.0	100.0	100.0	100.0	100.0	100.0	87.6	94.8	91.8	12.4	5.2	8.2	—	—	—	—	—	—	—	—	—

TABLE 164—Foreign-born Jewish first admissions with psychoneuroses to all hospitals for mental disease in New York State, 1939–1941, classified according to nativity and use of alcohol.

Nativity of parents	Total			Abstinent			Moderate			Intemperate			Unascertained		
	M	F	T	M	F	T	M	F	T	M	F	T	M	F	T
							Number								
Russia	41	61	102	20	45	65	13	1	14	2	—	2	6	15	21
Poland	20	17	37	6	14	20	8	—	8	—	—	—	6	3	9
Austria	10	23	33	4	20	24	3	—	3	—	—	—	3	3	6
Germany	6	12	18	3	5	8	3	4	7	—	—	—	—	3	3
Hungary	4	7	11	3	7	10	1	—	1	—	—	—	—	—	—
Roumania	—	9	9	—	9	9	—	—	—	—	—	—	—	—	—
All foreign-born	97	134	231	43	101	144	31	6	37	2	—	2	21	27	48
							Per cent								
Russia	100.0	100.0	100.0	48.8	73.8	63.7	31.7	1.6	13.7	4.7	—	2.0	14.6	24.6	20.6
Poland	100.0	100.0	100.0	30.0	82.4	54.1	40.0	—	21.6	—	—	—	20.0	17.6	24.3
Austria	100.0	100.0	100.0	40.0	87.0	72.7	30.0	—	9.1	—	—	—	30.0	13.0	18.2
Germany	100.0	100.0	100.0	50.0	41.7	44.4	50.0	33.3	38.9	—	—	—	—	25.0	16.7
Hungary	100.0	100.0	100.0	75.0	100.0	90.9	25.0	—	9.1	—	—	—	—	—	—
Roumania	—	100.0	100.0	—	100.0	100.0	—	—	—	—	—	—	—	—	—
All foreign-born	100.0	100.0	100.0	44.3	75.4	62.3	32.0	4.4	16.0	2.1	—	0.9	21.6	20.2	20.8

TABLE 165—Foreign-born Jewish first admissions with psychoneuroses to all hospitals for mental disease in New York State, 1939–1941, classified according to nativity and time in United States prior to admission.

Nativity	Total			Less than 1 year			1 to 4 years			5 to 9 years			10 to 14 years			15 years and over			Unascertained		
	M	F	T	M	F	T	M	F	T	M	F	T	M	F	T	M	F	T	M	F	T
											Number										
Russia	41	61	102	—	—	—	3	—	3	2	1	3	—	2	2	33	55	88	3	3	6
Poland	20	17	37	1	1	2	1	4	5	3	—	3	7	1	8	8	11	19	—	—	—
Austria	10	23	33	—	3	3	3	4	7	—	—	—	—	—	—	7	16	23	—	—	—
Germany	6	12	18	—	10	10	3	—	3	—	—	—	—	—	—	3	2	5	—	—	—
Hungary	4	7	11	—	—	—	1	—	1	1	—	1	—	1	1	2	6	8	—	—	—
Roumania	—	9	9	—	—	—	—	—	—	—	—	—	—	—	—	—	9	9	—	—	—
All foreign-born	97	134	231	4	17	21	14	8	22	6	1	7	7	4	11	63	101	164	3	3	6
											Per cent										
Russia	100.0	100.0	100.0	—	—	—	7.3	—	2.9	4.9	1.6	2.9	—	3.3	2.0	80.4	90.2	86.3	7.3	4.9	5.9
Poland	100.0	100.0	100.0	5.0	5.9	5.4	5.0	23.5	13.5	15.0	—	8.1	35.0	5.9	21.6	40.0	64.7	51.4	—	—	—
Austria	100.0	100.0	100.0	—	13.0	9.1	30.0	17.4	21.2	—	—	—	—	—	—	70.0	69.6	69.7	—	—	—
Germany	100.0	100.0	100.0	—	83.3	55.6	50.0	—	16.7	—	—	—	—	—	—	50.0	16.7	27.8	—	—	—
Hungary	100.0	100.0	100.0	—	—	—	25.0	—	9.1	25.0	—	9.1	—	14.3	9.1	50.0	85.7	72.7	—	—	—
Roumania	—	100.0	100.0	—	—	—	—	—	—	—	—	—	—	—	—	—	100.0	100.0	—	—	—
All foreign-born	100.0	100.0	100.0	4.1	12.7	9.1	14.4	6.0	9.5	6.2	0.7	3.0	7.2	3.0	4.8	64.9	75.4	71.0	3.1	2.2	2.6

Index